THE CURSE OF ESTACADO

Book One in the Series

Trails of Blood and Wine

PAUL AND MERRILL BONARRIGO

The Curse of Estacado
Book One in the Series
Trails of Blood and Wine

Copyright © 2022 Merbon

All Rights Reserved

Publisher: Merbon
4401 Old Reliance Road
Bryan, Texas 77808

979-820-1238
TheVineyardDistrict.com/story/

Copyeditor: Lynette M. Smith

Softcover ISBN: 978-1-7361770-1-3
eBook ISBN: 978-1-7361770-3-7

To our children, Paul and Karen Bonarrigo,

And our grandchildren, Paul Anthony and Sophia,
the next generation of
Texas wine pioneers

Acknowledgments

This book could not have been completed without the efforts and support of a number of individuals, and among them are the following.

We, in the wine industry, are all grateful to Dr. Roy Mitchell, Dr. Charles McKinney, and Dr. George Ray McEachern for their belief in and contribution to the Texas wine industry. Together, they helped to create the Texas Wine and Growers Association, which represents Texas grape growers and wineries by providing marketing assistance, educational programs, and legislative representation.

Tim Dodd, Director of the Texas Wine Marketing Research Institute, and Natalia Velikova, Associate Director, have offered their unwavering support over the years and assisted the industry.

Jeff Cope, Russel Kane, Ron Saikowski, Nan McCreary, Dale Robertson, Shelly Wilfong, Jessica Dupuy, Melanie Ofenloch, Rob Moshein, Rebecca Castillo, Reggie Solomon, and Andrew Chalk continue to tell the Texas wine story.

Monie Smith has provided the beautiful floral designs, and Don Smith has shared his wise guidance.

Finally, the authors would like to thank all the many individuals who have not been mentioned by name in this book, for their unique contributions.

The Trail of Blood and Wine:
The Curse of Estacado

Chapter 1

My father rarely spoke of his heritage. His Native American facial features and our name, Talan – which might have been Anglicized- pointed to Native American genes.

He entered the army at an early age. His career took him all over the world. He was a Colonel with the United States Army and had great responsibility for his brigade of soldiers. It kept him busy. So, I knew my father as "The Colonel," a leader of men.

During most of my life, Dad was deployed, and the family stayed home. He visited us between deployments. When Dad came home, we celebrated. Mom cooked his favorite meal, rack of lamb with mint sauce. She was the picture of calmness as she prepared for his homecoming. "Trevor, check to see if the ice has been delivered. We'll need it when Dad arrives. He'll want to rest with a drink." "Trevor, see if the bread has risen enough to touch the dish towel." "Trevor, will you..." I was busy all afternoon but being busy kept the butterflies in my stomach a little calmer.

I respected my father but hated how the army separated our family. I know my mother felt very alone. I could hear her crying after each long-distance call with Dad. It made me sad to see her upset. I hoped that soon Dad would retire, and our family could be reunited.

Mom taught school and was the foundation of the family. She taught English and was a school counselor. My friends constantly told me, "You are so lucky to have your mom. She is so understanding." "She helped me take the right courses to get into college." "Your mom wrote me the best letter of recommendation." Mom was a mom to all her students. Her golden hair and sweet, gentle temperament were perfect for her life as a teacher. The students called her Ms. Lily.

She was named after her grandmother, Lily. They gardened together as Mom grew up. Grandmother Lily was known throughout the county as having the prettiest gardens. Mom grew Grandmother's famous root beer lilies. Bulbs from her original garden traveled with us whenever we moved. The speckled yellow and sienna petals drew those passing by to stop and look. The strong scent of root beer brought them closer. It was fun to watch. Later we would see them in the soda shop asking for a root beer. It was my favorite soda drink.

Mom loved gardening – digging out weeds and cutting flowers. We always had cut flowers on the table. I worked with her in the garden whenever I could. She gave me the love of nature and the desire to be a steward of the land. She even tried to grow a small vineyard, but the harsh winters of Lawton, Oklahoma made it difficult.

Sunday dinner was special. We worked together in the kitchen to make my favorite dish – Roulade. She learned to make it from Grandmother Lily and taught me the family recipe. Every Sunday I heard her call, "Trevor, tenderize the meat and bring me the pickles from the pantry."

Mom's German Roulade

Ingredients:

1 pound veal cutlets (1/8 inch thick)
Mustard
Dill gherkins
All-purpose flour
Oil for frying
Salt, pepper, and dill weed to taste

Cut veal lengthwise into 2-inch-wide strips. Season on both sides with salt, pepper and dill weed. Brush veal with a thin coat of mustard. Please a gherkin on each strip; roll up and secure with a toothpick. Dredge lightly in flour. Heat the oil in skillet; fry roll-ups until golden brown (do not overcook, as veal will become tough). Drain on paper towels.

Serve with mustard cream sauce or remoulade.

Mom's roulade was amazing. She was the best German cook in Lawton. Mom's family was from

9

Hof, Germany. Hof is a Bavarian town located on the Saale River. It was a border camp for the American 2nd Armored Cavalry Regiment after World War II on the border of Germany and Czechoslovakia.

Grandmother Lily was born and raised there. She told me, "The American soldiers were truly kind to us. They appreciated a good home cooked meal. Mother and I would make roulade for the American soldiers. They helped us escape to America."

Grandmother Lily was short in stature yet large in personality. Once I interviewed her for a high school history report. She told me, "Hof was a staging town for the German Army during World War II. German soldiers were everywhere. At the beginning the soldiers were eager and proud to serve. As the war continued, life became very difficult. Food supplies became short. Many residents were accused of being spies.

"All the men of Hof were drafted into the military. Even the young men as young as sixteen were taken into the military." Grandmother worked in the post office processing mail to the German troops.

"Occasionally a letter was damaged, and I opened it. It broke my heart. I read how lonely the troops were and how they longed to be home with family. I realized that this was not between the citizens of our countries but between the politicians. The soldiers were someone's family members longing for the same peace and love we desired."

After the war, Hof was on the East/West German and Czechoslovakian border. The army troops assisted Grandmother Lily with her immigration papers and one year later she came to America through Ellis Island.

"The Americans were very kind. They helped us as best they could. Thousands came from other countries looking for the hope America's freedoms seemed to promise." She moved to Lawton, Oklahoma, where the army had a base. She learned English but as she aged her German language became more prevalent.

Military families make large sacrifices. When my dad deployed, Mom had to be my mom and dad. Also, she was busy assisting the families of those who were deployed with my dad. With all the responsibilities she had with school, she never missed my sporting event and had a nice hot meal for me when I got home.

In Little League I watched longingly as the boys playing catch with their fathers. Dad gave me a baseball. "Hey, thanks, Colonel. Do you have time to play catch with me?" "Uh, no, Son. I need to go through my gear and get things ready. I leave at five in the morning." Acid from my stomach rose into my mouth, and I fought to keep back the tears. I thought as I turned and walked out into the yard, "not again. Didn't the ball come with games of catch?" I don't think Colonel even noticed the tears streaking down my cheeks.

Several days later, as we pulled into the driveway after school, Mom looked over at me. "Hey, Trevor, how about we see how we can pitch that new ball? It's been a few years, but I used to play ball with my brother and cousins. Are you ready to play?"

I hid my surprise as I ran inside to get the ball hoping we could do our practice in the backyard out of sight from the neighbors. That was the beginning of our regular after school routine of playing catch. I know Mom tried. I even found a library book that she was reading to help her learn about baseball. Looking back, I was not as grateful as I should have been. She really tried to fulfill both mom and dad roles.

Mom even taught me how to fish. Behind the house there was a pond. For my birthday she gave me a cane pole. "Trevor, grab the shovel from the barn and let's go find some worms." She let me find the biggest worm. We sat on a log on the shore of the pond. She put the worm on my hook. "Trevor, hold your cane pole out over the water. Slowly let the worm fall to the bottom of the pond." She reached over and gently wiggled my fishing line. "Mom, I got a bite!" "Hold it firm, Trevor. Don't pull back too fast. You might jerk the hook from the fish's mouth." She guided my hand and helped me bring in an eight-pound bass. That night dinner was delicious.

She bought me my first bicycle and then took me on my first ride. I remember her holding on the to the seat to steady me as I wobbled down the street. She kept saying, "You can do it! You are doing it. Great job!" Grinning, I turned to look at her and realized that she had released the seat and I was riding on my own.

I was an only child and learned early to entertain myself. Reading was my favorite pastime. Mom encouraged me to read at least one book per week. "Trevor, have you finished your book this week?" "What was your book about this week?" She even gave me a test once just to assure that I was reading them!

During high school I loved reading history and spent my study hall hours in the library studying Texas history. The books were filled with Texas heroes. Mom made me cream cheese and jelly sandwiches. "Mom, look at the label on the jelly jar. Davy Crockett said, 'Make sure you're right, then go ahead.'" "That is good advice," she said. My favorite heroes were Daniel Boone and Davy Crockett. I even had a coon skin cap that I got when Mom took me to the Alamo. The heroes in the books were heroes like Dad.

After school, I played football in the fall and baseball in the spring. I remember looking up to the stands and seeing my mother sitting alone. Don't get me wrong. I was super proud of Colonel and never met anyone more patriotic. I just always hoped that he would be more dedicated to being my dad and I was jealous of his time away from me in the Army.

Memories came from places we went and people we met while dad was deployed in Italy. He took us to the countryside where I saw beautiful vineyards and wineries. Festivals were everywhere, and every celebration seemed centered around the wines of that region. People would smile, laugh, make toasts with wine glasses, and spend hours talking about the vintages and the *terroir,* those elements of a location, soil, climate, and land topography that make a wine growing region unique.

My dad's favorite duty station was Sigonella, Sicily a joint services NATO base. There Dad served with navy, air force, and marines and with other military officers from Italy, France, and Germany. We lived in Catania. Dad commuted to the base each day. Mom and I explored.

I shared with her all that I found. "What an amazing city filled with so many secret places! Did you know it has a gate from the 16th century?" "There is an ancient Roman bath under the square in front of the cathedral. They discovered it while drilling to install piers for a statue. Suddenly the drill broke through into a huge empty space beneath the square. When they went down into the hole, it was an ancient bath area. Can we see it?" I thought about how that bath was just waiting patiently all those hundreds of years to be rediscovered.

Mom became a great cook of Italian food. I even got more time with my dad, watching and playing soccer together. I visited Palermo, Augusta, and Syracuse, and had the best gelato in the small village of Gualtieri Sicamino.

My fondest memories and happiest days were when we visited the beautiful Greek Amphitheater in Taormina and when we went skiing on top of Mount Etna. In the spring, the smell of lemon blossoms filled the air all over the island.

Dad's last duty station was at Fort Sill in Lawton, Oklahoma. When he retired, I could tell Mom was relieved. She would no longer have to be both mom and dad and would no longer worry about his safety in unknown locations. I felt such a contented joy to have them both with me. I hoped to have a real relationship with my dad, but I had to go off to college. This time I left him; he did not leave me.

Chapter 2

At State University, my life was filled with studies and time with new friends. Some of my friends were of Native American descent. We talked for hours about their ancestors. They shared stories about Native Americans roaming the plains, hunting buffalo, and celebrating a Spirit that cares for the Earth. They learned of their heritage at home around the dinner table.

The Comanche, called "Lords of the Plains", were the dominant tribe on the southern Great Plains in the 18th and 19th centuries. The area around Lawton was part of what was called the *Comancheria*, which included large portions of present-day Texas, Colorado, New Mexico, Oklahoma, and Kansas. The Comanche ruled over it.

My friends described the historic range lands as lush green pastures that attracted large numbers of buffalo. They said, "The fields were carpeted with beautiful wildflowers of all colors. Wild fruits and berries were abundant." Visions of their ancestors filled my head. I found myself wondering more about my heritage. Was I descended from the Comanche? As my friends shared photos of their families, suddenly I became acutely aware that I had similar facial features. They said, "You could be our brother."

My history professor, Dr. Robin Graves, gave me some books to read. "Dr. Graves, can you meet with me and my Native American friends to talk about the stories they have shared?" We began meeting once a week at the library. She came early and had something new to share each time. "The Comanche lived in regional tribes. Each tribe had a chief. The chief was responsible for his people. The primary source of food and other resources was buffalo. Reservation life that the US government offered had very few buffalo. The tribes feared starvation." My cheeks felt hot to the touch and my head started pounding. I tried to hide my anger and sadness at the treatment of these great peoples.

Christmas was always special at our home. Mom would decorate every room, bake all the family favorites, and have Christmas carols playing all day long. I looked forward to heading home and seeing mom and dad.

As I drove across the Texas High Plains, the expansive southern region of the Great Plains, I imagined what it would have been like to roam this vast prairie, live in a tipi and dress a buffalo. My heartbeat faster just thinking about chasing the buffalo on horseback.

There were no markers in this ocean of flat lands – no trees, no shrubs, or landmarks. I could see why ancient travelers would have staked the routes to create markers for others to follow. They called it "Staked" Plains or in Spanish - "Estacado".

The road sign for Fort Sill greeted me. Something deep inside me felt strangely connected to this place. I had so many questions about Fort Sill, Native American history, the Native American culture in Oklahoma, and the settling of the High Plains and the Estacado of Texas. Fort Sill would give me clues about the name *Talan*.

Mom and Dad greeted me at the door. They were both smiling and eager to hear all about my studies and friends. They showed me through the entire house to see the Christmas decorations. Mom said, "Your eyes are twinkling like the Christmas lights. It is so good to have you home." She gave me a big hug. All the stress of school evaporated in her arms.

While home, I went to the Fort Sill Museum to learn more about Native Americans. Dad suggested that I also go to Quanah Parker's house. Quanah Parker was a Comanche Chief who led his people to the reservation.

Fort Sill is a large army base located in the middle of Indian reservations. At the museum, I met museum curator Helen Wells. She was generous with her time to show me around. "Fort Sill was established in 1869 by Major General Philip Sheridan to control Native American attacks in the High Plains." With a wink she added, "The United States government also wanted to acquire more lands."

I told her that Dr. Graves had told me that the US government promised the Comanche $1.25 per acre and one hundred sixty acres per tribal member in exchange for Native American lands. As I repeated this, I could feel my blood pressure rising. "The injustice!" I blurted out.

Helen looked at me and grinned. "Do you mean Dr. Robin Graves?" I said yes with a confused look on my face. Helen laughed and said, "Robin was my roommate in college. What a small world." Is it true that President William McKinley confiscated two million acres from the Comanche?, I asked. Helen responded regretfully, "They paid the Comanche less than $1.00 per acre and worse, they gave no assurances of owning land." She looked at me as though to look into my soul, "Can you imagine our government of the people, by the people and for the people having so little compassion for these Native American peoples" My stomach tightened, and my face turned red again.

Everywhere I went in Fort Sill, there was more history. With thirty-nine Native American tribes headquartered in Oklahoma, history resources are rich and abundant. I was amazed that even the name *Oklahoma* comes from two Native American words that when combined mean red person—*uka* meaning person and *huma* meaning red. Even Texas comes from the Caddo Indian word *Teysha*, meaning *hello friend*. I laughed inside, thinking about my Texas friends. They are fitting examples of friendliness.

My next stop was Quanah Parker's house. A sorrow came over me as I stood at the front door. His pride must have been dashed, and what a sense of failure he must have experienced. Kelven Arrow, the tour guide Helen had arranged to meet me, greeted me at the door. Kelven told me, "Quanah was proud of his heritage. He even lived in a tipi on the reservation for many years. This house was built for him and his wives and children in later years." "Do you think he felt the house was a betrayal to his heritage?" Kelven did not answer.

I remembered that my friends had told me Native American people followed the buffalo across the Texas Panhandle thousands of years before the first settlers arrived. I felt the freedom they must have sensed as they moved from Oklahoma to Texas and back. There were no state lines, borders, or restrictions. It was all one land of the Great Spirit.

I knew my friends would be so interested in all that I had seen and learned. I came away from Quanah's home respecting how Texas history was so intricately connected with Oklahoma through the Native Americans. It was obvious to me that Native

American history requires understanding Texas history.

I shared with my dad what I had learned. He looked at me with a smile and said, "I have someone I want you to meet."

Chapter 3

Dad took me to a local coffee shop. At the counter sat an elderly man who had long gray hair and a leathery, wrinkled face. Dad led me to him and said, "Bill, this is my son, Trevor. Trevor, this is Bill. Bill was my history teacher." He went on to say that Bill was part Native American and part Mexican American and was an expert in Native American history. I couldn't wait to hear his story.

After introductions, we ate together at the counter. Bill said, "Did you know that Francisco Coronado was the first Spanish Explorer to arrive in Texas?" That surprised me. What did Coronado have to do with Native Americans? I listened. Every other sound in the diner disappeared. It seemed that only we three were there.

Bill went on to say, "Coronado was born in 1510 in Salamanca, Spain. He came to the New World and explored Mexico and the Southwest of the United States from 1535 until 1542. While in Mexico, he was befriended by Antonio Mendoza, the Viceroy of Mexico; and there he met his wife, Dona Beatriz, the daughter of a wealthy New Spain family. Do you know why Coronado came?"

Continuing, he speculated, "Coronado wanted to prove himself worthy, so he set out to make his own fortune in 1540 with three hundred Spanish soldiers and one thousand Native Americans." I was fascinated, wondering how Coronado organized and led one thousand Native Americans! Bill went on to share, "As the youngest son of a wealthy Spanish aristocrat, Coronado knew that he would not inherit his father's fortune. He had to create his own."

From my high school history classes, I remembered that Coronado had heard of a wealthy land called City of Gold. Bill said that the pursuit of the City of Gold led Coronado to the Plains Native Americans. His expedition for gold was unsuccessful, but he did discover the Texas Panhandle, Palo Duro, later dubbed "the Grand Canyon of Texas," and the Native Americans who lived there.

Bill said, "There is evidence that they tried to settle the land as they explored. They built missions in those areas, taught the natives about God, and encouraged the native peoples to plant farms." He went on to explain, "Through the priests, the Native Americans were exposed to crops grown by the Spaniards, which included European grapes. These were used in making wine for Holy Communion."

Bill joked, "Priests taught the Native Americans better wine making methods so the priests could get better wines. They gave each Native American family forty grapevines to plant because they wanted to encourage the tribe to settle down. They needed to be less nomadic and less dependent on the buffalo. My family was one of those that received these grapevines." Chills went down my spine. I was looking at a pioneer family of Native American grape growing in Texas. "Those Native American families planted small grape vineyards from Menard north towards Amarillo."

"I was particularly interested in the fact," Bill said, "the Native Americans were making wine 350 years before Coronado arrived in the Texas High Plains." He said that wine residue was found in pottery used by Native Americans. The Comanche collected wild grapes, placed them in ceramic jars and fermented with wild yeasts. After two months, they had wine. The wine was used in ceremonial festivities. Thanks to the Native Americans and the Spanish explorers, Texas had vineyards before most of the United States.

Dad and I finished eating, thanked Bill, and headed home. I had signed up for a leadership conference that was being held in Lawton over the holidays, so I had to leave the house immediately for the opening session. Really, I wished I could have stayed longer to talk with Bill.

At the leadership conference, I met John Ferris. He was an enthusiastic, happy-go-lucky horticulture student at Texas A&M University. We became good friends. His family was originally from Portugal, and they owned vineyards in Temecula, California. We shared our vineyard experiences and excitement about the burgeoning wine industry.

Since he was away from home for Christmas, I invited him to dinner. Mom was delighted to have another guest at the table. "Thank you for inviting me, Mrs. Talan. Can I help in the kitchen?" Dad and I followed John into the kitchen. We all sat around the kitchen table, talked, and hand-rolled her Mama Rosa meatballs – a recipe she had learned in Sicily.

Dad asked John why he was going to Texas A&M University. John explained, "When I was in high school, I met Tom Plant, a famous wine writer and tour guide from Temecula. Tom shared vineyard and winery stories about his travels. One day Tom told me a story about his trip to Texas wine country. It sounded fascinating," said John. "I knew that someday I would own and run my family's Temecula vineyards." "Tom suggested I learn about this new wine region and referred me to Dr. George McEachern at Texas A&M University. Dr. McEachern was teaching viticulture courses there."

John's face lit up as he said, "I flew to College Station to meet Dr. McEachern. George Ray, as he liked to be called, picked me up at the airport and drove me to campus, where he had arranged for me to stay in a Corp of Cadets dormitory." John said, "George Ray is a jovial storytelling Cajun from Louisiana." "I felt like I got a PhD in Texas wine just by listening to George Ray in the car ride from the airport."

While there, John said he went to an Aggie football game. "I have never seen such spirit at a school," he said, and quipped that he had to get better shoes because his feet hurt from standing the entire game—Aggie tradition requires it. John was hooked! He told us he immediately applied to Texas A&M, joined the Corp of Cadets, and became a "gung-ho" Aggie.

After the holidays John and I each went back to our respective schools with the agreement that we would someday work together to help the Texas grape and wine industry. John and I stayed connected during college. We shared information from our classes on Texas viticulture, and we each attended the other's graduation. I got a job as teaching assistant in the viticulture department at State University. John went to work at wineries in the Estacado and in the Hill Country.

John helped the wineries improve wine quality by growing better grapes and by using better wine yeasts and better sanitation practices in the wineries. He also had to learn about the rules of selling wines in Texas. There were so many laws that inhibited sales of Texas wines.

Cotton, Texas, was considering going wet. This meant that alcohol could be sold in that area. The Cotton Chamber of Commerce contracted me to do market surveys about the desire of Cotton residents to make the area wet. The Chamber wanted to know consumer attitudes before they officially endorsed the issue. I called John for help. The chamber asked us to determine how many wine drinkers were in Cotton and what impact going wet would have on the Texas wine industry.

John and I began investigating by interviewing all the liquor stores on The Strip. Cotton was a dry city, which meant that alcohol could not be sold in grocery stores. The only location where alcohol could be sold was a small strip of land south of town along the major north-south highway. Locals referred to it as *The Strip*. There were so many neon lights on The Strip that I felt like I was in Las Vegas. The Strip consisted of a half dozen retailers, and most of their business was beer. Wine sections were small. You could hardly find any Texas wines. When we asked why the selection was so small, the stores would say that no one buys wine, and no one knows about Texas wines.

Store by store, we talked with owners and managers. None of the liquor stores supported Cotton's going wet. The manager of Frank's Liquor told me, "The liquor stores on The Strip have a monopoly. We are fearful that if the grocery stores are allowed to sell beer and wine, it would reduce our business."

I went to restaurants and asked servers, "What type of wine do you have?" The servers said, "Red, white or rosé." When I asked for the brand, they had no clue.

We did customer surveys to identify wine buying habits, as well as attitudes toward buying local wines.

What did we learn?

John and I staked out at stores to watch behaviors. On any given Friday, there would be large crowds of consumers stocking up for the weekend. The stores on The Strip even had drive-through pickup so that people who did not want to be seen in a liquor store could buy their alcohol and remain in their cars, out of sight. I saw some of my neighbors in that line. I waved at one of them and they ignored me. John said, "Religion has a profound impact on consumer behavior."

In addition, we did in-store interview surveys. "Excuse me, are you familiar with Texas wines?" "Did you know that we grow wine grapes in Texas?" "Have you tasted Texas wines?" We learned that most Cotton wine drinkers knew little about Texas grape growing and Texas wine. Only 16 percent of Cotton wine consumers interviewed had ever had a Texas wine. The majority of those who had drunk Texas wine said they would buy it again. Our conclusion: the major obstacle to growing the market for Texas wine was to educate the consumer about Texas wine.

John and I thought access to buyers might be a problem for Texas wines. What we learned was that Texas wineries could sell directly to stores and restaurants, as well as out of their tasting rooms. Out-of-state wineries were not allowed to sell directly to the retailers. They could sell only if represented by a distributor. We thought this was a great educational opportunity. Wineries could present directly to the buyer and the consumer.

The problem was that if wineries sold direct, then distributors had little interest in representing their brands.

Our mission became to educate and to help Texas wineries grow.

Chapter 4

John and I began to give talks on our market research. The local newspaper did a feature article on us mentioning us as consultants. Leon Xider contacted me about a project. He was one of three attorneys who were looking for land. "My partners and I are interested in developing a vineyard and winery near Cotton. We would like you and John to be part of that project." This group was determined that Equoni, the name they had already chosen, was to be the best winery of all in Texas—the biggest, the best, the most luxurious. They asked if John and I would be interested helping their soil scientist find that perfect spot. We jumped at the opportunity.

I contacted the soil scientist, Robert Stratta, and met him at the Cotton Experimental Vineyard. He was humble and easy-going and had vast knowledge and passion for his work. Robert and I sat and talked about his life, his work, and this project. He shared, "I went to Central University. My family has been farming for generations. I worked beside my mother and father on the dairy farm since I was a boy. We got up with the sun and worked from dawn until dusk, doing what I saw as hard labor.

"We weren't wealthy, but we had a wonderful family relationship, and my parents were dedicated to get me a college education. While in school, I became more interested in the academic side of agriculture."

He told me how he appreciated his family's support and that he had vowed to give back to his family. I related because I felt the same about my family.

Robert developed an interest in grapes at college. "My professor had me plant vineyards around the state. With the landowners' permission and support in growing, I planted ten varieties in five distinct locations around Texas. The plantings included Cabernet Sauvignon, Merlot, Tempranillo, Riesling, Zinfandel, Chenin Blanc, Chardonnay, Muscat Canelli, Lenoir, Sauvignon Blanc, and a new grape Blanc du Bois." As a result, he became known as a grape expert and when he graduated from college, he consulted with new vineyards in Texas.

I asked him what he discovered. He shared, "Lenoir and Blanc du Bois grapes performed best in East Texas. In North Texas Cabernet Sauvignon and Merlot performed best. In West Texas Tempranillo performed best. In the Texas High Plains all the varieties did well except Blanc du Bois. In Fort Stockton Chenin Blanc, Sauvignon Blanc, Chardonnay, and Muscat Canelli performed best."

Robert talked about his family often. I could tell that he was devoted to them and deeply loved his wife. He told me, "I proposed to my wife on the summit of Pikes Peak because it symbolized my devotion to her." I thought that was sweet and had to have required much time and planning. He shared that he was a deacon in his church and offered to pray for me and shared his faith.

I could tell he was compulsive about things. He showed me his notes regarding the vineyards he was consulting. They were listed in alphabetical order, time dated, and were highlighted and color-coded.

When I asked how he met Leon, Robert confided, "On one of my consulting jobs I was approached by three attorneys in Cotton who were interested in getting into the wine business. They asked me to find the absolute best place to plant a vineyard and a winery in the Texas Panhandle. He said he began looking in Plainview and Floydada, as there had been vineyards planted in each location. He went to Plainview to visit with Freddy and Rodney Bell, the Bell Brothers. They were well established vineyard operators in Hale and Lamb counties. Freddy and Rodney told him that in the early '80s they had had remarkable success. But in the nineties, herbicide overdrift, hail, and spring freeze reduced their yields.

Robert then looked in the area around Patricia, Texas. "I found the soil to be too sandy with a high probability of nematodes, a bug that loves to eat the roots of plants."

He asked John and me to join him in his tour of the Panhandle. John introduced Robert and me to a friend of his father. John's dad and Kevin Hill were friends in college. John said, "Kevin is an internationally renowned geologist from Shreveport, Louisiana, who's familiar with soil types and geology all over the Southwest." Kevin indicated that a combination of both sand and loam was most desirable and said we could find that soil more central to Cotton. So, Robert and I started doing soil sampling around Cotton. Sampling the soils reminded me of Mom and the time we spent working in the garden together. The smell of the dirt was different but good.

While Robert consulted with the three attorneys, he developed a friendship with them. He took John and me to dinner to meet them. Leon Xider, Elliot Prudence, and Phillip Brief were there. It was a lovely meal, but Robert consumed much more wine than I expected, and I drove him home. A week later, Robert and I went to lunch. He drank a full bottle of wine himself. I warned him he had better watch himself. He was such a good man, and I hated to see that he was drinking too much.

When I drove him home, I met his wife, Mary, whom he met while at Central University. She was a math teacher and was not fond of Robert's fascination with wine. I really liked her. She seemed embarrassed. "I grew up in a family that did not consume alcohol," she said. "I love him so much," she shared, "but I fear what appear to be signs of

Robert's excessive drinking." She told me she tried to help him stop, but Robert was determined to please his new friends. "He thinks they can make us rich and provide him the opportunity to give back to his family."

The attorneys brought Robert in as a partner for his services in finding the absolute best location for the project.

Robert was obsessed with the soil. Following Kevin Hill's lead, we drove around and around until we found the perfect soil. It was located east of Cotton on rich, sandy loam with chalky limestone beneath it. In studying wine making, my enology classes taught me that limestone soils create a minerality in wine that the wine world celebrates.

Much of the land had been used for grazing cattle, so there was plenty of rich soil enhanced by the cows. While driving, we saw a Federal Landbank sign advertising the sale of one hundred acres. I called the number on the sign, and Melissa, the property's listing agent, answered. She shared that the owner of the land, a South African physician practicing in Lamesa, Texas, had passed away. His widow could no longer make payments on the property, so the bank had repossessed it. While we were in the car, Robert called the attorneys and told Leon to contact Melissa.

Chapter 5

My curiosity about these risk-taking attorneys that I had met at the dinner with Robert was peaked as I listened to their discussion about this project. I did recognize one of them at the dinner. Robert introduced him as Elliot Prudence, the attorney who would represent the partnership with the Federal Landbank. I recognized his name, as I had seen him originally at a Cotton fundraiser where he flamboyantly bid on every auction item. I introduced myself to him and he told me he was from Houston. Elliot was not a person you forget.

Robert added to the story, "Elliot put himself through law school in Houston. To save money, he lived at home with his parents. With savings and real estate connections he had met through his mom, he began to invest in houses to flip. He made his money by buying older homes, refurbishing them in his spare time, and selling them for a profit." Robert spoke about Elliot with evident admiration.

I asked Elliot how he knew so much about wine. He said, "One of my real estate connections, Trish Baldwin-Hagner, a realtor, was a member of a wine organization, the Knights of the Vine. She invited me to join. As a member of the Knights of the Vine, I was able to socialize with wine lovers." Robert said it made him feel important and accepted.

I asked him what the organization was. He replied, "The Brotherhood of the Knights of the Vine is an international organization created to promote American wines and other wine producing regions. The membership includes wine professionals and consumers. Educational programs and tastings expose consumers to appreciate wine quality. The Houston chapter is one of the largest and well-respected chapters." That sparked my interest. Consumer education. Promotion of American wine regions. That is what John and I were committed to do.

Elliot beamed, "The Knights of the Vine even elevated me to Master Knight." He often spoke of Lady Master Commander Gaye Platt and Grand Commander Buddy Hagner and Trish Hagner. "They taught me so much about wine and offered me the opportunity to travel all over the world to visit wine regions." He explained to me, "The Knights of the Vine was rooted in the ancient days of France when knighthood was by royal decree. The first knights grew vines, made wine, and tasted the wines as cup bearers for royalty."

Elliot shared that he met his wife, Cynthia, in Houston at Sharpstown High School. "She was very bright and could have gone to medical school, but her family didn't have the money, so she got a nursing scholarship to Baylor. She became an outstanding nurse at Methodist Hospital, working with Dr. DeBakey." Elliot said that he and Cynthia came to Cotton because it was a booming area for medicine. "Cynthia worked with the first Cotton medical team to do heart transplants." It meant a lot to him that when he joined Leon Xider's law firm in Cotton, Cynthia began taking classes to become a nurse anesthetist.

Leon Xider, son of the firm's owner, took Elliot under his wing and introduced him in all the Cotton social circles. Elliot loved wine and shared bottles with the other attorneys. That is how the other attorneys got interested in wine. He had made frequent trips to California. Elliot's favorite wine became Caymus red blend. He had a collection of more than three thousand bottles in his wine cellar and was proud to show them off.

I joined all the attorneys at a Grape Day held at Doc McPhearson and Dr. Reed's vineyard. Dr. Bill Lipe, the horticulture specialist in Cotton, was doing a presentation on how to establish a vineyard and what grape varieties were doing best in the Texas High Plains. Dr. Lipe spoke in the morning. Dr. Roy Mitchell and Doc McPhearson spoke in the afternoon about launching a successful winery. Dr. Tim Dodd, Director of Texas Wine Marketing, talked about wine marketing. The information was so fascinating that I became a member of the Texas

Wine and Grape Growers Association. The attorneys took a liking to me, since I teach viticulture at State. They all took me under their wings. I felt like I was a partner, too. They even asked me if I was interested in investing, but I told them I had no money.

At the meeting, I remember tasting wines from Pheasant Ridge, Glasscock Vineyards, La Buena Vida, Messina Hof, and Llano Estacado.

Another attorney partner was Phillip Brief. He was a trust attorney who did trust work for the biggest bank in Cotton, the National Farmers Bank. His relationship with the bank made him the perfect collaborator with Elliot in the purchase. Phillip was originally from Cotton and went to Law School in Cotton. His family was a High Plains multigeneration cotton farming family. Phillip married Linda, a young lady from St. Louis. He said, "She just seemed to pop into Cotton one day. I thought she was such a beautiful woman." He was also impressed that her family pioneered the High Plains from St. Louis after the Indian Wars. She went to school in Canyon, Texas, near Palo Duro Canyon and studied history at State University. She was now a history teacher at a Cotton High School.

When I asked Phillip why he was interested in the winery, he confided in me that he had already made and lost a fortune. He said he was constantly looking for the next great deal and speculated on land all over West Texas. He even bought land in Plainview prior to a wet/dry election. He remembered, "I paid too much, but I was certain that Plainview would vote wet. When the election failed, I had to sell the land at a big loss. Only then did I realize that Plainview is the home of strong anti-alcohol groups. I had no idea of their influence in the community." I remember him saying about every bad deal, "It is better to have loved and lost than never to have loved at all." His conservative wife, Linda, tolerated Phillip's gambling ways for the sake of the family.

Phillip knew the least about wine and depended on Elliot. I saw that Phillip liked sweet white wines and his favorite was Messina Hof Winery's Angel Late Harvest Riesling. He told me he was trying to develop a taste for reds. He felt that if he drank reds, he would seem more like a sophisticated wine drinker. And he had heard that red wine was good for you.

Phillip shared how hard his father had worked as a cotton farmer. He admitted to having no interest in cotton farming, so that is why he went to law school. I could see Phillip had a gambler's personality. He was constantly betting on outcomes and talked enthusiastically about going to Las Vegas. Getting into the wine business and all its challenges was a business risk he was willing to take.

Phillip said, "My father could use some red wine because he has a bad heart." He went on to say, "My dad expressed concern about the number of new vineyards planted on land that had been cotton land. He knows the importance of diversified agriculture and he really needs to diversify, but he relies on cotton as a one-year crop so he can borrow money, plant the cotton, harvest the cotton, and pay off the loan." The vineyard business is vastly different. It takes three years to make the first crop and about seven years to break even.

At Grape Day I had the opportunity to get to know Leon Xider better. I learned he went to school back east at Columbia Law, where his dad had attended. He was a divorce attorney. The Xider family was from Amarillo and had cattle ranches. Leon and I shared a common interest in cattle, since my family ran cattle in Oklahoma. After he completed law school, he returned to Texas where he went to work at his father's law firm and met a sweet Texas girl, Susan Bee. I met her as well at Grape Day. She was a paralegal who had gone to Uplift Junior College. Her father worked at the John Deere place in Levelland. Leon was the senior partner at the law firm.

The Xider Law Firm was the most prestigious law firm in West Texas, and its advertisements were all over the television in Cotton. Leon's dad, a well-known attorney, represented the most influential families in Texas. Leon had a lot to live up to. He was living in the shadow of a larger-than-life man. Leon told me he looked forward to making it big in the wine business so he could make a name for himself. He also wanted to bring honor to the firm and receive the blessing of his father.

He invited me to fly with him. His hobby was flying planes, which came in handy because The Xider Law Firm had offices in Amarillo and Cotton. He would fly to Amarillo each week.

Leon wanted to know about my interest in Texas wineries and vineyards, and I shared my experiences. Leon said, "This new winery is a sure thing, and I can see the future is bright for the Texas wine industry. With the right land and the right winemaker, it cannot fail."

All three attorneys were good friends. They were members of the country club, played golf together, socialized together, and were well known in the community. They had strong connections with the media and Cotton city government support for the project. After going to Grape Day, they felt that they knew all the key players in the Texas wine industry.

Chapter 6

Phillip Brief called and invited John and me to join him and the partners for dinner. He thought we could provide insight on the negotiations. The attorneys were meeting with the Federal Land Bank representatives at the Crazy Door restaurant near State University. The Crazy Door has great food. Elliot ordered his favorite wine, the Caymus red blend. The bank repeated what the listing agent, Melissa, had told me: that the South African physician who had owned the property had dreamed of planting a vineyard there but had unfortunately passed away suddenly before the project could begin.

The bank representative mentioned there had been a water well on the property, but the well dried up. "The neighbor property has a fabulous water well, and the owner was willing to lease his water," he said.

The attorneys had been aware of all the foreclosures in town and had investigated them. The bankers told the attorneys that another party was interested in purchasing the property. I saw the attorney's bristle. I could tell their sense of urgency and the familiar relationship they had with the bankers was rushing them into the purchase. The attorneys told the bankers to draw up the paperwork.

The next day Robert said, "Well, Trevor, we signed the papers." He laughed nervously. "Now we only have to produce the $500,000 to pay for the one hundred acres." Fortunately, the land was east of Cotton in the wet precinct that could sell wine.

The partners asked me again if I was interested in investing in the winery. It sounded enticing, but I had to turn it down for lack of funds. They purchased the property with the five-hundred-thousand-dollar loan from the bank but wanted to do a public offering to do the construction, so they rolled the purchase of the land into the public offering.

To secure the two-million-dollar loan for the property, all three attorneys had to pledge their profit-sharing plans. Even Robert Stratta had to contribute. He told me, "I had to mortgage my home as collateral for the loan and Mary wife was very unhappy about it." She had told me she could see his personality changing under the stress. "He is easily angered and interacts with the family less and less," she lamented.

Elliot confidently assured everyone, "When we go public, we will secure enough money to pay everyone back. This is only a temporary inconvenience."

The attorneys contacted a major brokerage firm—
Gorg, Perce and Fientin—a big firm out of New
York to make a public offering. It just so happened
that a classmate of mine worked there. I shared the
information with Leon. The brokerage firm sent
prospectuses all over Texas. Major funding through
the banks was difficult because grapes and wine were
considered speculative. None of the Texas wineries
at the time were making money.

The public offering generated $10,000,000. The
attorneys and I got together and toasted the success.
They even bragged that they had contracted
$8,000,000 of architectural plans by the firm of
Latour & Margo out of Sonoma to design the
winery, do the dirt-work and the vineyard, pour the
foundation, and set aside a reserve fund for interior
decorating.

Robert Stratta, John Ferris, and I worked together to
lay out the vineyard. The mornings were cool and
crisp. We got up early. The sun was rising in the east,
and there was no wind blowing. We were able to lay
out the vineyard and planted ten varieties and ten
acres each.

The ten chosen varieties included Cabernet
Sauvignon, Merlot, Chardonnay, Pinot Noir,
Sauvignon Blanc, Zinfandel, Cabernet Franc,
Riesling, Gewurztraminer, and Sangiovese. Robert
contacted the next-door neighbor about using his

well water. He said that the neighbor was a Native American who was genuinely nice. He allowed us to connect our irrigation to his well. We used drip irrigation and vertical shoot position in the training. Grapevines came from Inland Dessert Nursery in Washington State. All the vines were planted on their own roots. We took the chance that phylloxera would not be factor. Phylloxera is an insect that eats the roots of European grapevines.

The partners invited me to fly to New York, but I was busy teaching classes. I told them to tell me all about it when they returned. In New York there was a showing of Pierre Letrec, a world-renowned sculptor, and Mary V, an abstract expressionist painter. The partners were impressed by their works and bought forty-seven of the sixty sculptures at the showing and ten paintings by Mary V. The sculptures depicted man's struggle over adversity. The partners seemed to relate to it. Mary V's art reflected a colorful and vibrant *terroir*.

The partners all believed it was important to have a fabulous well-designed building that is beautifully decorated. They felt the interior portrayed the image of success and were committed to presenting a first-class operation.

When they returned home, Leon told me that he took his partners to all his favorite places in Little Italy in the Bronx, where they ate clams on the street, and to the Half Moon restaurant, where they had the best pizza ever. Leon enthusiastically shared, "I took them to Bryant Park and Central Park and for lunch at the Oak Room in the Plaza Hotel."

"We even met up with my college girlfriend, Bebby Finegold. Back in college, she attended Barnard while I was at neighboring Columbia. We'd met at a dance and then dated for a while. Today, she is the wine writer for the *New York Times*. I hope that she can help us once the winery is complete."

I recognized her name. Bebby Finegold had become a leading voice in wine media. Her endorsement of the partners' wines could help launch the brand.

"While in New York, we met with major wine retailers to get an idea of their interest in Texas wines. They were not aware that Texas made wine but were fascinated about the novelty of a Texas wine." He said that the retailers advised them that a winery is only new once, so it was critical that the first new wine releases were successful and won gold medals in international competition. The retailers advised the partners to enter the new wines in the San Francisco Chronicle Wine Competition, the San Francisco International Wine Competition, and the Los Angeles International Wine Competition. A big win at any of these competitions would launch the brand.

The partners also realized that a poor showing in competitions would slow the progress of the brand.

Leon, having gone to school at Columbia, showed the partners around the city and campus at Columbia. "The night before we left, I took them to the Rainbow Room, where we listened to the music of Ella Fitzgerald. We celebrated the public offering, our architectural masterpiece, and the collection of bronzes and paintings we procured." They came home feeling incredibly positive about the prospects of the project.

Chapter 7

The remaining $2,000,000 was not enough money for finish out, winery equipment, or grapes. The attorneys went back to the brokerage to ask for more money. The brokerage said no. My friend who worked there confided in me that it had been difficult getting full subscription on the initial offering.

The partners estimated it would cost an additional $5,000,000 to complete the building and purchase the winery equipment. They agreed to pony up and began to pledge to the bank their remaining assets. They went all in, pledging farms, homes, and personal assets. Robert even went to his father to ask for money from the dairy farm. His father said, "Absolutely not." They filled me in on their plan and asked me again if I wanted to become a partner. I started to feel very suspicious of the deal.

They got the loan and were in huge debt.

The partners developed a fondness for vineyards and wines and my insatiable thirst for more knowledge. All four of the partners asked me to fly out to California with them so they could purchase the wine equipment and barrels. The Unified Wine and Grape Symposium was taking place there, and it was the perfect time to see everything about the winemaking industry.

We visited Scott Labs and bought lab equipment and a new state-of-the-art Wilmes fourteen-ton press. They purchased their pumps and stemmer-crusher from Prospero Equipment. I will never forget Prospero's booth at Unified. They had a whole Prosciutto that the owner, Tony Prospero, had cured. He was serving paper thin slices on bruschetta. It was delicious and reminded me of my days in Sicily when my dad was stationed there. The attorneys purchased their barrels from Yuri De Leon of World Cooperage. It was nice to meet the owners of Inland Desert where we had purchased the grapevines. While at Unified, we saw so many famous winemakers—Robert Mondavi, Chuck Wagner, Zelma Long, and so many more. We tasted amazing wines.

The partners were newbies who had the Texas mystique in their cowboy hats and boots. They really stood out on the convention floor. I had imagined that the Californians would be vegetarian surfer types. But they were very down-to-earth, relaxed businesspeople. The California wineries were many. Though Texans were few they were confident in the dream of making it big in a new wine growing region.

I was surprised that Leon expressed appreciation, "We were fortunate that great West Coast wineries took us under their wings. We got so much advice we could write a book." I wish they had listened, but the advice seemed to go in one ear and out the other. The partners all agreed they were going to do it the Texas way. They were going to get rich their way.

While in California, they interviewed potential winemakers and hired Tym Winter, a winemaker from California who had worked in Sonoma. Tym got his degree from the University of California at Davis. He had never been to Texas but could see the opportunity. I thought he was arrogant, his pride fueled by his belief that he was far better than any other winemakers in Texas. He even told me how much the attorneys had offered to pay him. It was far more than any Texas winemaker was making at the time. It was clear to me that the attorneys had extremely lofty expectations of Tym's winemaking skills. I gave them my opinion, but Tym's résumé blinded them. I was suspicious of his commitment and personality.

Once we were back in Texas, the equipment started arriving. The first project was to get the crush pad installed and organized, since it would not be long before harvest. The crush pad is where the grapes are received after harvest and where the process of winemaking begins. Next to be installed were the destemmer-crusher, built in Italy, and the brand new Wilmes press with the latest technology from

Germany. They got the best pumps to use in transferring grapes and must, the skin and juice of the wine, and got the forklift ready. The state-of-the-art stainless-steel tanks from Santa Rosa Tank Company were installed, and refrigeration was added. The service man from the Cotton Refrigeration Company told me that they had never installed a chilling system for a winery, but they were confident that their engineers could do it. The last of the equipment to arrive were the French oak barrels stained and coated with a mildewcide. The red painted hoops of the barrels looked like they had just come out of a French Chateau. They were stacked neatly in the refrigerated barrel room. The winery was set, ready to go, and it looked amazing!

Then the next task was to secure grapes for the upcoming harvest. The partners knew that the vineyard we had planted would not have its first harvest for three years. It was customary at the time to contract for twice as many grapes as you might need. Usually something like hail, spring freeze, wind damage, herbicide overdrift, etc. would reduce the crop size. So, if a winery needed 50,000 gallons, they contracted 100,000 gallons, expecting the crop to be half.

Tym secured eight contracts which would normally produce 50,000 gallons, 50 percent red and 50 percent white. Winemaker Tym impressed the growers with his Sonoma winemaking background and then paid way too much for the grapes because his frame of reference was Napa Valley grape prices. I cringed. Was it that he was a newcomer, or was his arrogance a curse?

Tym asked me to help with the harvest, since he would lose his way when driving out to the vineyards. I was happy to help make the first harvest the best. Like the New York wine retailers, my mom had also told me you can only be new once, and this was the winery's moment to be new.

The first harvest was an exceptionally abundant crop year, and it produced double what they expected to receive in gallonage of contracted juice. The growers had difficulty estimating the size of their crops. Tym did not help them. They would take samples, but Tym insisted that the growers run their own chemistries.

Texas growers were not accustomed to doing juice chemistries. Tym expected them to test sugar content, run Ph, and total acidity tests. Usually, growers took grape samples to the winery and the winery ran the tests. Crop estimates were done together with the winery. Tym's attitude and expectations resulted in unnecessary errors. When the grapes were harvested, the crop-load estimates and chemistries were way off. As a result, very few harvest days had correct tonnage. Grape chemistries were in error when the grapes arrived at the winery, and Tym would have a temper tantrum every time it happened. I cannot tell you how many times he called me to say that Texas grape growers were screwing up his reputation. It happened frequently.

Chapter 8

As a California winemaker, Tym was accustomed to perfect grapes. Texas grapes had chemistries with high Ph and high sugar contents. None of his winery staff had any winery experience. Tym insisted that all the growers had to begin picking at 2:00 a.m. so that everything could be harvested before sunrise. The growers had never done this. Tym insisted that the grapes arrive no later than 7:30 a.m., at the beginning of the production shift. He would not receive any grapes after 4:00 p.m. I overheard conversations where he yelled and cursed at them. I wanted to jump in and apologize, but it was not my place.

The partners left wine production completely to Tym. Their attitude was that they were paying Tym a lot of money, so he was to get it done. The partners visited the winery and took their friends on tours of the facility. When Tym was asked how things were going he said, "Everything is great!" Then he would confide in me that everything was falling apart.

When the grapes started coming in, Tym decided that all the wines needed to be cold settled. This meant that the juice went into a tank chilled to 35 degrees, just above freezing, for twenty-four hours. The purpose of cold-settling white juice was to clarify the juice to prevent off aromas. Cold-soaking red grapes causes the red skins to extract more color and flavor prior to fermentation. I teach in one of my viticulture elective classes that these steps are risky because volatile acid can infect the juice.

Tym and the partners soon realized that the refrigeration system had insufficient tonnage and could not achieve those temperatures. Tym asked me if I knew of a refrigeration contractor, but I told him there was no way they could install a larger compressor at harvest time. I did mention it to the partners, but they said there was no money for a larger refrigeration system.

The wines began to spontaneously ferment with wild yeasts and could not be cold settled. Worse yet they began to have a rotten egg smell. Tym had no experience in dealing with these kinds of problems. In Sonoma, Tym rarely had to lower the Ph of the wine. The refrigeration systems he had worked with in the past had been oversized so that cold settling was easily accomplished.

One morning we walked into the fermentation room and were overwhelmed with a terrible smell. The wines were sick. Tym had tanks that got so hot they started to overflow because the wine liquid expanded above the tank capacity. Tym became increasingly more defensive and began blaming the growers for their farming practices. This made the winery very unpopular with the growers.

The partners asked if I would be willing to help the growers harvest and coordinate the transportation to the winery, since Tym was so busy attending to fermentation problems. Thinking it would be a broad experience, I volunteered to do it.

Tym got the white grapes into the winery. He expected 25,000 gallons of white juice but received 45,000 gallons instead.

The harvest proceeded through August and into the first week of September when the red grapes were ready to be picked. Then the rains came. The High Plains of Texas are subject to September rains due to Pacific Coast hurricanes. Instead of picking on September 7, they had to wait ten days for the grapes to dry out. It rained every day. I went to survey the vines, and there was rot everywhere. Tym insisted that the growers spray even if it was raining. Tym was a prima donna and was not good for Texas wine.

When he started receiving the red grapes, he ran out of tank space. The winery was full of 5,000 gallons of red juice and 45,000 gallons of white juice. Tym told the red grape growers that they had to find other homes for their grapes. I was shocked and told Tym and the partners this would not go well with the growers.

He cancelled 90 percent of the red contracts. Since the growers had to then find secondary contracts with other wineries, many of them could not place all their production and received 50 percent less for those grapes they were able to sell. Grower contracts were usually written for multiple years and secured future revenue for the growers. They could take the contract to their banks to secure loans for farm equipment. Whenever the contracts were cancelled, the banks could demand repayment of the loan from the farmer. This could produce a financial disaster. Immediately, the winery obtained a bad reputation with the growers.

At the conclusion of harvest, we had a blind tasting of Tym's wine. I was invited. It was a blind tasting with Tym and the partners. It was eye-opening. The wines were thin and oxidized and had no varietal character. Tym concluded that he needed to go back to Sonoma. The first week in October, just as the winery was having its grand opening, he left his keys on his desk and disappeared. No note, no notice.

Chapter 9

What a predicament! The partners were in the project for $16,500,000 and had burned bridges with the growers.

The red grape harvest was very brief. Only twenty-five tons of red grapes were delivered to the winery. Once Tym departed, the turmoil in production stopped. Antonio, the most senior cellar hand, and I stepped up and finished the harvest as well as fermentation. The red wines turned out much better than the white wines. The event side of the winery operations also had problems.

Expecting to pay for the grapes and staff from events at the winery, the partners were surprised to learn that no events had been booked. They had hired an event planner to secure weddings at this beautiful new venue. They just knew the State University graduating students would want to have their graduation parties and weddings at this architecturally awarded winery. Unfortunately, the event planner had no experience or motivation; her compensation was not tied to her sales, so she waited for calls to come in. Then when the calls did come, she would wait days before she returned the phone calls. When she did meet with customers, she was completely ill prepared and unprofessional.

I became increasingly involved in the winery. Thank God I had no money in it. The preharvest grand opening was postponed until October because the equipment came in just before harvest and there was no time for planning.

The partners remembered what the New York retailer said: "You can only be new once." The grand opening was particularly important, a gala affair. The local newspaper, *The Cotton Glacier*, called it the event of the decade. The *Texas Biweekly*, one of the biggest magazines in the state, was there. All major newspapers, *The Wine Proliferator*, and the *Wine Gazette*, were all there. Wine writers from California came. Leon Griffith came from the *San Francisco Chronicle*. I got to meet Leon Griffith. He was a founder of the Wine Institute and wrote books about wines of America. I asked him what he thought of Texas wine. He said, "They have enormous potential. Texas has the right soil, climate, and grape varieties. Now Texans need to be fans and advocates of Texas wines."

Unfortunately, though the building was beautiful, there was no Equoni wine ready to serve. There were wines in tanks and barrels, but they served California wines. The attorneys were so snobby that they talked badly about other Texas wines. They felt that their wines would revolutionize the Texas wine industry, so they refused to serve Texas wines.

The *New York Times* sent correspondent Bebby Finegold, Leon Xider's former girlfriend from college days, to see this project and attend the gala. He had not seen her since his partners met her in New York.

Leon introduced her to the other partners' families. They took her through the art and bronze statue collections and the building. She was from Connecticut and had been writing at the *New York Times* for ten years and was fascinated by the concept that Texas would produce wine. Her major was journalism, with a minor in art history.

After the partners met her in New York, Bebby wrote an article in the *New York Times* on the future of this new Texas winery. While she was visiting, she outlined a plan on how to get good publicity on the project. "Do a press release on the architecture and wine development each month. Once you have entered wine competitions, every gold and silver medal should receive a special press release as soon as you get results. Create a special wine premier event for wine releases annually and send new wines to all major wine writers at least two months before they're released to the public."

After the gala, a friend of hers at *Modern Building Digest* did a feature article on the splendid architecture of the building and art. As a result, it won numerous awards.

Two hundred guests received invitations to Equoni's gala grand opening. The partners asked me to get eight of my students to help with the gala. Each guest received the invitation etched on an empty Equoni wine bottle. All two hundred invitees attended, including the governor. The Crazy Door restaurant catered a food-and-wine-pairing feast. Appetizers were served with a lovely sparkling wine from Gruet Winery in New Mexico. Lobster was flown from Maine and served with a barrel-fermented Russian River Chardonnay. Broken Arrow venison was served with the Caymus red blend.

I gave tours of the facility and vineyard. The guests could see baby grapevines growing in the hundred-acre vineyard.

As the guests arrived, they were greeted by the partners' wives and two amazing statues that welcomed the guests as they entered the majestic, ten-foot-tall, French oak double doors. The eighty-four-foot wine bar was to the left. Each guest was offered a glass of the Gruet sparkling wine. We had met the winemaker at Unified and were fond of his sparkling wines. Who would have thought you could make such good sparkling wine in New Mexico! Caviar and pâté hors d'oeuvres were tray passed.

Guests were escorted into the stainless-steel fermentation room and then to the crush pad.

Finally, all the guests were seated at long, white linen-draped banquet tables set among the barrels. Braided grapevine runners graced the center of the table. Gold-leaf candles scattered along the runners glowed with a soft but bright light. During dinner, the attorneys unveiled the new colorful label art and shared their vision of the winery. I had never seen anything so elegant, so well produced, or so expensive.

The gala was extremely successful, and all the media had wonderful things to say about the architecture and the hospitality. Unfortunately, none of the media comments were about the wine because there were no wines ready to be served.

The next day I had the opportunity of driving Bebby Finegold to the Cotton airport so she could catch her flight back to New York. On the way to the airport, she commented that she looked forward to tasting the new wines. She was disappointed that the Equoni wines were not ready for tasting.

While Bebby was in Cotton, she had an opportunity to taste other Texas wines. She had a favorable impression of the Texas wine industry and saw its enormous potential. She did confess to me that she feared the attorneys were spending too much money on "show" and not enough on the wine. When she got back to New York, she authored a wonderful article on Texas wines. It just did not include ours.

Chapter 10

Equoni Winery had secured International Distributors statewide in Texas with hopes of national distribution later. International was established in 1916 by the Brazier family. In the early days, the business sold flavored soda. Immediately after the repeal of prohibition in 1933, they began distributing beer and branched into wine and spirits. It is still family owned and operated, and they also distribute in New York.

International was anxious to taste the wines to setup distribution plans for the upcoming holiday season. We pulled tank and barrel samples and sent to them.

International Distributors was disappointed with the samples, but the winery property was so impressive, and the media coverage the winery was receiving was so positive, that the distributor agreed to take on the brand. International delayed the release of the wines until June of the following year so the wines could be fixed and re-blended.

This was devastating news for the partners because they were counting on the large windfall of cash from distributor sales in the fourth quarter. Now the winery asked me to tell the growers that they would not be paid until June of the following year. What made matters worse was that there were wines that needed to be fixed, and the California winemaker had left town to go back to Sonoma. The partners promoted the most senior cellar hand, Antonio, as winemaker. And Elliot, with his vast knowledge of wine, stepped in to assist in fixing and re-blending the wines so that they would be acceptable to the distributor. I even started working in the winery on my days off.

In addition, the distributor told them that the winery had to pay sales incentives to the distributor salespeople and provide marketing funds to promote the wines after the wines were released in June. It cost $25 to $50 per wine placement for a salesperson to put the wine on a wine list, even though the wine may only appear on the wine list for three to six months. They even asked the winery to pay for fishing trips to Mexico or trips to Italy for the campaign to be executed. This meant that Equoni Winery would have to produce $250,000 for marketing at the same time the payment on grapes was due. I had never had any contact with a distributor. I thought the distributor was responsible for brand building. Not so. The winery builds the brand, and the distributor delivers the product. It was an eye-opening experience.

Elliot and recently promoted cellar master Antonio worked together day and night to fix the problem wines. By March, they were ready to send another round of samples back to the distributor. Even though I had no money in the partnership, I was all in. I felt that these wines were mine. God, I prayed International would like them. This time International said that the wines were acceptable—not extraordinary, but acceptable.

The attorneys remembered what Bebby Finegold had told them—that they should enter the wines into prestigious wine competitions one month prior to release. The partners sent samples to Bebby Finegold and to notable international wine competitions. Bebby called Leon, "Leon, these wines are ok. They are not stunning. It would be best if I do not write about these. Let's wait until the red wines are released. Send the red wines when they are ready."

We entered the white wines in the San Francisco Chronicle Wine Competition and won six bronze medals. Despite winning bronzes, the winery sent the wines and press releases to national media. Just as predicted, the winery received zero media attention for six bronze medals. They had spent $900 on entries and more than $2,000 for the press release and received no favorable media attention. My winemaker friends say, "Getting a bronze medal is like kissing your sister. It is not going to get the winery any media coverage."

I had worked at a wine competition once and realized how subjective the results can be. In wine competitions, panels of judges score each wine blind, which means without seeing the wine label. A double gold is equivalent to ninety-five out of one hundred points, and all the judges must agree on the double gold medal. A gold is normally ninety-two out of one hundred points. A silver medal is normally eighty-five out of one hundred points. A bronze medal is usually eighty out of one hundred points. Fewer than 5 percent of wines entered usually receive a gold or double gold. Usually, 10 to 15 percent of the wines entered receive a silver medal, and 30 percent of the wines entered receive a bronze medal. In most prestigious wine competitions, a bronze medal means that the wine is commercially acceptable but not distinguished. Rarely is a bronze medal given any media recognition.

Between October and March, events began taking place at the winery, and Equoni wines were being sold at the tasting room. Unfortunately, the amount of revenue coming in barely covered the note payment. The realization of potential foreclosure was openly debated among the partners. My stomach was sour, and my head pounded in empathy with the partners, their families, and Leon Xider. His father had warned him, but Leon could not accept this conclusion. The reputation of the law firm was at stake. His relationship with the rest of his family was at stake. Failure was not an option. He had to find a fix for their situation. Leon had to preserve his relationship with his father.

After the wines got into the marketplace, the partners began to receive cease-and-desist letters from other wineries who saw that the labels infringed on their trademarks. This took the partners by complete surprise. They thought, if the name were not duplicated exactly, it would be okay. That was not the case.

Trademark infringements are very costly to fight. One of the most notable was Goats Do Roam. The French region of Cotes Du Rhone said Goats Do Roam implies it came from the French region. It had been in courts more than five years and cost the wine company more than $1,000,000. Our attorneys did not have that kind of money.

The winery received so much national publicity that the West Coast wineries were aware of the labels. When Tym, the California winemaker, returned to California, he stirred the pot by telling them that the labels were like well-recognized brands in California. I knew he could not be trusted. The artwork was almost identical to well-known brands. So, the attorneys had to negotiate a "use up," which meant they could use the labels for six months to sell what they had in inventory. Then they had to replace the old labels with the new ones. The problem was that it would create a great deal of confusion to launch one label and then six months later have a different label. This would not help with brand identity or development.

The wines were selling very slowly off the shelf, and distribution was not expanding as fast as the attorneys thought it should. Leon Xider confided in me that the bank contacted them because they were slow to make their monthly payment. The bank even called John's father, who was on the board of directors, asking what was up. That night Leon's father had a very stern conversation with Leon. He said Leon had to "fix this now." Leon told his father they would do what they had to do.

The partners were tapped of money and started selling off things to liquidate. I started seeing things being sold off and staff laid off. Foreclosure became the conversation of the partners. The bank began to repossess things. The first items to disappear were the bronze statues. They sold at auction for ten cents on the dollar.

That satisfied the bank, but the partners still needed additional cash. They decided to reduce the price of the wine so it would move faster. The distributor agreed and alerted the retailers. There was minimal increased movement in wine sales.

They lowered the prices of the wines in the tasting room and made an offer to their VIP customers of

25 percent off case purchases. The partners soon learned that lowering prices signaled to the industry that a problem was brewing. Once prices are lowered, it is virtually impossible to ever raise them back to initial levels. The vultures of the wine industry were circling.

Chapter 11

The financial woes of the partners were negatively affecting their family lives. "They are drinking more, staying out late, and arguing with their spouses. Our children are being bullied in school because of their fathers' tarnished reputations in the community." The growers' children had heard from their own parents how the partners had failed to pay them.

I lost many grower friends. They knew it was not my fault, but their hatred of the winery rubbed off on everyone. The domino effect on their lives became clear. One thing after another seemed to fail or fall apart, and the loss of the business became increasingly more apparent.

The law firm was losing clients. Leon was affected most because his family had owned the law firm for two generations. Newspaper articles raising questions of the insolvency of the partners and their businesses became community gossip. I have never seen so much family trauma. These were my friends who were being torn apart.

Mary shared that she began working more to bring in more money to support their home. She took on tutoring jobs in the evenings and weekends.

Leon's wife, Susan, had already given up her salary at the law firm. She took on more work as a court reporter.

Elliot Prudence's wife, Cynthia, stopped her training as a nurse anesthetist and took on additional shifts at Cotton General to help with the family income. She felt guilty because Elliot was the real estate attorney and should have done more due diligence before getting involved with the winery property.

Elliot called a meeting of the partners. "I have influential oil and gas friends in Houston. Let me make an appointment with them to see if I can get money by bringing them into the winery project as additional partners." The partners agreed.

His long-time oil friends who were also members of the Knights of the Vine included the presidents of major oil companies. The plan was to fly from Cotton to West Houston airport, which was a public-use airport near the petroleum corridor on the west side of Houston. They were to take the executives to Messina Hof Harvest Green Winery and Kitchen in Richmond, Texas, also on the west side of Houston. The chef at the Kitchen was excellent, and Elliot knew that if he could give the executives a great meal and world class wine, he could convince them to become partners. This would provide them with the needed funds to continue to operate.

Elliot even invited me to go along. I was disappointed that I could not go; it would have been great to see if the partners could pull out of their dire circumstances.

Leon said, "Let's fly to Houston to make this presentation and meet these execs. I am happy to use my plane and we will get there faster, and it will impress them."

The partners were unaware that Leon had not flown his plane to Houston in years. Leon was not accustomed to flying such a long distance. When he would take his family to Houston to visit friends and family there, he would normally drive, and site-see along the way.

I met Leon at the Cotton airport early before the rest of the partners arrived so that I could see how he checked out the plane. "Before flying," he said, "I have a system of evaluating the emergency and safety systems of the airplane." He showed me the instruments. I noticed that he seemed concerned and asked why. "There is a Blue Norther blowing in from New Mexico, but if we leave on time, I think I can beat the front." That was a concern. Then, he mumbled under his breath, that, due to his lack of funds, he had been unable to maintain his plane properly. "I have to do the maintenance myself," he said.

As we were finishing the inspection of the plane, Leon received a call from Elliot, who reported that when the partners went to pick up Robert Stratta to take him to the airport, Robert was not at home. They asked his wife, Mary, where he was. She began to cry, and while weeping she admitted that Robert was at a bar in downtown Cotton. They arrived at the bar and discovered that Robert was drunk. "We are on our way to the airport," reported Elliot, "but we stopped at a coffee shop to try to sober him up and are running late."

Leon was pacing around the plane, angry and frustrated with Robert and the partners for being late. He filed his flight plan and listed in the logbook the names of all his partner passengers. The flight plan included flying over Post, Snyder, Sweetwater, Abilene, Temple, College Station, and then into West Houston.

The partners arrived. Robert apologized for his behavior. He felt responsible for the delayed departure from Cotton. I wished them well and waved goodbye as they taxied away.

Takeoff was smooth, but I could see that the front was approaching. In West Texas, when the wind starts blowing you can see the soil and dust of New Mexico in the air. Skies are big and land is flat, so you can see an exceptionally long distance.

The flight seemed to start fine. I watched until the plane was just a little dot in the sky. Leon had told

me that during the flight they planned to discuss
their presentation to the oil executives.

Chapter 12

After the plane took off, a feeling of sorrow for the partners came over me. They and their families had become like my family. I hoped and prayed that this last-ditch effort would result in a new life for the winery.

About an hour later, I got a call from an air-traffic-controller friend in Abilene. I had told him that the partners would be coming through his airport. He said, "Trevor, I am so sorry, the partners' plane crashed just west of Abilene." At first, I didn't believe it. How could this be?

According to my friend, "The pilot called in on his radio that as they were flying over Sweetwater, there was a loud noise, and the plane began losing altitude. A bird flew into the engine, and the engine caught fire. Leon transmitted the distress signal notifying our traffic control in Abilene. He requested permission for an emergency landing at Abilene Regional Airport."

My friend reported that firetrucks and sheriff's deputies drove rapidly out to the crash site. He said, "Emergency medical personnel attempted to administer lifesaving aid to the partners. It was too late. All four partners died. I am so sorry for your loss." I didn't know what to do. Should I call their wives? My heart sank, and I felt sick.

How ironic that four people could have so much bad luck.

It was a sad series of events. I lost four friends. Numbness struck me as I realized I could have been on that plane and died with them. What about the families of these partners? They would be devastated. Before I had the chance to notify the partners' wives, I heard on a Cotton radio station that there had been a plane crash killing three prominent Cotton attorneys and an unidentified male.

Once word got back to Cotton, it immediately made the lead story on all the TV stations. My phone started ringing. It seemed that every newspaper, radio, and TV show contacted me. The newspapers started with the story but then went on to write about the winery and each of the partners. It became a media frenzy. The reporters went out to the widows' homes. The widows heard about the accident from the news media. The whole community was in shock. It had significant impacts on lives and businesses. The banks were owed a lot of money. The growers were owed a lot of money. The suppliers to the winery were owed a lot of money.

Their deaths remained the top story in Cotton for a week. Robert Stratta's wife, Mary, called me sobbing, "Trevor, you will not believe this. The bank is

already calling all of us to see what our plans were."
She just cried and cried on the phone. I felt helpless.
She said," All four widows want to get rid of this
winery as soon as possible. It ruined our finances,
our families, and our lives. It is cursed!"

The bank repossessed the property and began the
process of finding a new owner. The property had
gained a reputation of being bad luck, so it was
difficult for the bank to find owners and to recoup
the money owed to them.

The bank could not find a buyer immediately, so
they foreclosed and took over the operations. I
drove by the winery and felt a wave of sadness and
frustration come over me. The shareholders had lost
everything, including their lives.

The bank contacted me." Trevor, could you please
do labs on the wines to protect them the best you
can?" They also hired back Antonio as winemaker.
Finally, they hired a general manager, Walter
Hillman, with twenty years of experience in
California. At first, his connections in the industry
began to turn around the winery's fortunes. He
developed sales programs with the distributor,
Internationals, and took advantage of current trends
in the market. He and I met with the growers that
were owed money and convinced them to continue
to sell grapes to the winery and told them that they

would eventually be paid in full. I started to believe the winery had new hope.

Mr. Hillman met with civic organizations and the chamber of commerce. The civic organizations began having their weekly and monthly meetings at the winery. The chamber of commerce initiated a program of winery tourism promoting Cotton as a wine destination. They even established the Taste of Cotton, which attracted thousands of wine consumers to the area wineries. The Cotton chapter of the Texas Restaurant Association developed a Restaurant Week, where Texas wines were served exclusively at each of the Cotton restaurants and raised funds for the Cotton Foodbank. The Associations President, Lucy, had a vivacious can-do personality that helped to reverse the negative attitude towards Equoni Winery.

The winery coasted along for the next four years and was even able to break even. The growers got paid each year, and the wines improved. Mr. Hillman was in full control. I never heard from the partners' wives again. Robert's wife went back home with her parents. The Xider Law Firm sold, and Leon Xider's dad resigned from the bank board.

After four years, the Texas Alcohol Beverage Commission notified the bank that a bank cannot own the winery any longer and that they needed to find a buyer immediately. The Texas Alcohol

Beverage Commission had been very patient with the bank; but, as a public institution, the bank was not to own a winery.

Chapter 13

The bank found a group from Houston who were oil people. I got to meet them when they came to evaluate the winery deal. In fact, I recognized that some of them were the same executives that the partners were to have met on the day of their fatal flight. They were all wine collectors, members of the Knights of the Vine, and excited about the hype the winery had received; but none had any information about the issues the winery had faced. They asked me about the wines in process; they met with Antonio and had discussions with Walter Hillman.

The oil executives collected wine and liked wine, but they knew nothing about running a winery.

They paid the $7,500,000 owed to the bank and retained Walter Hillman as the General Manager. Each of the five owners were chief executive officers of large corporations. All the oil executives were in charge. It has been my experience that when everyone is in charge, no one is in charge. Walter was micromanaged by all five of the executives. He told me, "I have never in my life been bossed around like this." Each owner had a distinctively different attitude about how to run a business and how to manage people, and each of them had Walter's cell phone number. Walter had my cell phone number. He was used to running everything without supervision.

One thing that they all agreed on was to raise the price of the wines at once. Walter explained to them that International Distributors had required the winery to submit pricing for the entire year. Raising prices in the middle of the year was impossible. All the retail chains wished to have wine-supplier pricing for the year so they could establish their wine departments' schematic and promotion program for the year. Walter had also written wine sets in a previous job, so he knew how difficult it was to change pricing, especially moving prices up mid-year.

He told them that suppliers could change their pricing in December for the following year but not mid-year. You should have heard the owners. They were mad. They charged Walter to cut salaries and expenses immediately. The goal was to be profitable the first year of their ownership. Walter submitted a three-year plan to become profitable. The owners rejected it. Walter saw the handwriting on the wall and submitted his resignation. He was a professional and gave them thirty days' notice. He had all he could stand from the oil executives. They thought it would be easy to replace Walter. They were sorely mistaken.

Since I had been involved from the beginning, each of the owners confided in me. I felt like a priest hearing confession that could not be shared. Each of the owners had their own candidates to replace

Walter, so developing consensus on his replacement seemed impossible. Since they could not come to an agreement, they hired a firm to search for the replacement. Lawton Loper was a retiring beer executive from New England and was the best candidate the recruiting firm found. Lawton had friends at International Distributors, but they were all on the beer side of the distributor.

I tried to tell the owners that beer production and sales are vastly different from wine production and sales. The owners stubbornly believed that Lawton's experience with beer would be an asset in making the winery successful. He had no experience with wine and was not even a wine drinker. Lawton was hired and immediately started doing what his beer experience had taught him.

Lawton encouraged International to place the winery's wine in all the convenience stores throughout Texas, just as he had done with beer at his previous job. He had to pay large sales incentives to get case stacks of the wines in convenience stores, low-end grocery stores, and liquor stores. This was exactly the opposite direction the oil execs wanted. Their vision had been to create a luxury premium brand, but Lawton was creating a bargain brand. In his efforts to become profitable through expanded distribution and production, he miscalculated the impact of limited grape production. He had to maximize profit while knowing he could not significantly increase production due to limited grapes.

Although these powerful oil executives were expert in oil and gas production, they eventually realized that wine distribution and beer distribution were vastly different. Lawton stayed in place for six months. The five oil executives had their fill of the wine business and decided to have a nationally publicized auction. They called me to let me know. I thanked them politely but thought to myself, *I told you so.* The oil executives believed they could easily recoup their $7,500,000 investment.

The auction was publicized all over the world by articles in the *Wine Proliferator* and *Wine Gazette.*

Chapter 14

Now I was not only winery consultant but auction hand. The auctioneer called me to help with the auction. He asked me to pick up a new prospect for the winery. His name, Pedro Del Campo, sounded so familiar. Suddenly I remembered I had met him at Unified.

He was a California winery owner who had considered moving a second operation to Texas because it was centrally located in the United States, and he had heard good things about the burgeoning Texas wine industry. We exchanged cell phone numbers. He told me his family was a prominent one from Rioja, Spain. He left Rioja to make his own fortune. After attending the University of California at Fresno, he worked in the California wine industry in Paso Robles. There he met winemaker Don Brady. He said Don always spoke highly of Texas, where he began his own winemaking career.

At first, Pedro's attractions to California were the grapes, which grew well there, and the fact that much of the labor force spoke Spanish. He was extremely comfortable living and working in that area. He established a small premium boutique winery, making five thousand cases per year. International in California distributed his wines.

Pedro was familiar with Spain's primary grape, Tempranillo. Texas was gaining a reputation for growing extraordinary Tempranillo. As he was researching the Texas High Plains grape-growing region, he learned about the Spanish connection through Coronado and felt connected.

Pedro flew from San Francisco to Cotton. I picked him up at the Cotton airport. "Trevor, what a nice surprise to meet you again," he said with a big warm smile. As we drove, he commented, "Look at the high elevation and how flat the Texas High Plains region is! It reminds me of parts of Rioja. I wish my father could see this." As we drove up to the winery, the architecture made him even more excited about purchasing the winery. He was pleased to see the vines were trained up on the trellis and ready to produce fruit.

Fifty people attended the auction personally, plus there were buyers online. The auctioneer had ten phone lines, all busy. Bidding via phone opened at $1,000,000 by a bidder from Bryan, Texas. Pedro stood right in front of the auctioneer and raised his right arm in the air to raise the bid. The bids increased in $250,000 increments. Pedro never lowered his right arm. Bids from all over the world were shouted from the people staffing the phones and the people in the room. Pedro had an answer for each of them by raising the bid. The pace of the bidding was feverish. Four minutes later, Pedro's right arm was still up, and he was the winning bidder at $7,000,000.

"What a bargain," he said as he turned and looked at me in disbelief. "You should see what this place would sell for in California. My family will be thrilled." I asked him if he had conferred with them before he attended the auction. He said, "No, they will be excited about what I do in Texas."

Indeed, Pedro was elated. He came up to me and gave me a big high five. And then he immediately got on the phone to give the good news to his father and introduce me as his new Texas friend. He explained to his father where he was and what he had done. As he spoke to his father, I could hear his father's voice change dramatically from enthusiasm to anger. Pedro's face fell from jubilation to despair, right before my eyes. When he hung up, he just stood there with a blank stare. My heart hurt for him. He wanted his father's approval and attention just like I had wanted my father's approval.

I suggested we go to a local wine bar and talk. Pedro had much to share. "I am the firstborn son of the Del Campo Family. My family expected him to take over my family's wine fortune. I tried to work for my strong-minded father but could not. I made suggestions of modernizing the winery, but my father would not listen." Pedro shared that he aspired to succeed and show his father he could make it on his own. The California winery was doing well, but with this Cotton winery he could make it big. This Cotton winery would be that story that would make his father proud.

After researching his family, I learned the Del Campo family were excellent winery owners. They had operated successfully for generations, and they understood profit and loss statements.

The family asked for the sales records and due diligence reports on the business, which Pedro did not have because he had not asked for them prior to the auction. Once Pedro's family saw the books and realized how little money the winery was making, they told Pedro that they were not interested in buying the property. They said that he should have more thoroughly investigated the condition of the company.

Pedro had to produce 10 percent of the $7,000,000 within five days but could not. He looked at me defeated, "What am I going to do? I do not have that kind of money." So he went to the auction company to negotiate. Since he did not have the money, the auction company recommended that a second auction be conducted to get Pedro off the hook. Pedro was convinced that the second action would go for more than $7,000,000. He said he would pay the difference of what it would bring at another auction. If the second auction brought more money, then he would be making money on the sale.

The second auction was scheduled to be three months later. This time Pedro was responsible for the advertising. Pedro had no money to advertise. The auction company once again hired me to check the wines and help at the auction. Increasingly, I felt I was living in a nightmare. In fact, I began having nightmares about it but in my nightmares, I was the one having to come up with the money.

Many people in the industry were unaware this was a second auction of the same property. Only ten people attended, and very few people called in any bids. It only raised $2,500,000. The winning bidder was the Phlippo family. They had the opportunity of looking at the books. Having been in business for thirty years, they knew how to how to read a profit and loss statement and knew that the winery was worth only $2,500,000. That was all they bid.

Pedro was on the hook for the difference. So, he had to produce $4,500,000 without the help of his family. He could not. "Trevor, what have I done? This will bankrupt my California winery and I will be a disgrace to my family," he cried. I stayed connected with Pedro, but he was a defeated man. The winery had claimed another victim. I wondered when all this bad luck would end. I lost a friend and felt sorry for what had happened to him. He soon left California to go back to his family winery in Rioja. He was the prodigal son returning to the father. Yet another disaster had plagued the property.

Chapter 15

At the end of the auction, I met the new owners of the winery, Claire, and Luis Phlippo. They were from Fort Worth and had a distillery in the Dallas–Fort Worth metroplex which was very well known—The Phlippos'—and produced excellent gin. Luis Phlippo had come from an underprivileged home and had fought all his life for the rewards of success through arduous work. He was a staunch Republican and sat on the President's advisory council for exports. I was happy for them, as their bid was a significantly lower price than Pedro's, but I felt horrible for Pedro.

International distributed his gin all over the United States, and it was successful. The Phlippos had started this project together in his garage thirty years prior and just after they married.

Claire moved to Cotton, and we had lunch so I could fill her in on the winery's history. She started, "We will turn things around. When we work together, good things happen just like at Phlippo's." I could hear her hopefulness in her voice. She was so sure of what she and her husband could do. Claire had been the backbone of the Phlippo Distillery. She was the marketing genius of the business. Her family was well connected in Fort Worth.

Claire was responsible for much of the success of Phlippo Gin, but her husband Luis received all the credit. This was Claire's opportunity to be successful on her own. Claire had gone to college in Cotton. Claire thought she knew the Cotton wine market.

As soon as Claire moved to Cotton, she joined the Chamber of Commerce and met with city government introducing herself and pledging support and in turn wished to have their support.

She told me, "I met Luis on a blind date. He was from Southside, a high-crime area of Fort Worth." She recalled wistfully, "We had three dates before he proposed to me. I was captivated by Luis's good looks. We had a very lustful relationship. Our marriage was hot and at times very cold. It was a hard life. Luis stayed out late, visiting bars to generate business. Many nights, he would get home after midnight. I always waited up for him."

Claire called me to tell me that The Texas Alcohol Beverage Commission contacted them one month after the purchase, telling them that because they had a distillery, they could not own a winery. "They say you cannot own a winery and a distillery at the same time. Luis and I will develop a plan on what to do."

After creative thought, Luis presented the idea of getting a friendly divorce. He explained to Claire that he would own the distillery and take care of the estate, and that she would own the winery. They would still be emotionally married. He would soon get an apartment in Cotton, and she could stay in Cotton. They had been married thirty years and she trusted her husband, so they got the divorce, which allowed them to keep both properties. Two weeks later, Luis married his secretary. Claire called me, "I cannot believe this! My friends warned me about Luis. They said he was very flirtatious with women. I chose to overlook all his womanizing ways because he told me he loved me, he lavished me with gifts, and our business was doing so well. I don't know what to do."

Luis and Claire had lived in a lavish Highland Park estate of 10,000 square feet on two acres. Claire had enjoyed designing and decorating it. Together they had collected antiques to furnish it. Luis and his new wife lived there now.

Claire's family was proud of her success but never did like Luis and his untrustworthy ways. Luis was a wheeler dealer. He never looked anyone straight in the eye, and he reminded me of California winemaker Tym Winter. They were both shifty.

I grieved for Claire. She never suspected that Luis was having an affair with the secretary who was twenty years younger than him. Claire told me, "The secretary had fiery red hair, a flirtatious smile, and a possessive personality." Six months later, I read the news that Luis Phlippo was found dead in his bed. His secretary wife confessed to stabbing and killing him. Rumor had it that she suspected he had already begun an affair with a third woman.

Can you imagine how Claire must have felt? Not only was she shocked, but in the divorce, she did not request additional monies. She had trusted her husband and thought they were still a partnership. Instead, she owned a winery with no capital. He had run off with his secretary and had a thriving business. His adultery was no surprise to anyone else in the company. It was the ultimate betrayal. And when his will was read, his entire estate which included the distillery was pledged to the Republican Party of Texas.

Luis had managed all the production aspects at the distillery. He attended the University of Texas at Arlington, and his background was chemistry. Distillation was a natural extension of his studies.

In the second year, she got growers who would sell her the grapes and compassionate Texas wineries helped her make the wines. She was only making 10,000 gallons of wine total, and it was not enough money to sustain and pay the bills. Aggravating the situation was that her general manager was stealing from the till. She said, "He would come in late and leave early and stole well over $100,000." I had warned her a week after the manager was hired that I did not trust him.

She was devastated and did not understand what she had done to be so punished. She was embarrassed to ask her family for money. Her identity had been through the business she and her husband had built. The fact that he walked away and ignored the life and successes they had shared threw her into despair. When I could, I tried to cheer her up. But it was obvious that she was lonely and depressed.

Claire was such a sweet woman. She worked so hard to try to make the winery a success, but it did not work. She trusted too many people who were unworthy of her trust. She lacked capital and was new to the wine business.

She tried harder and worked harder, but it was too little too late. Claire had no choice. Her money had been completely depleted, so she contacted the auctioneer and explained to him that she wanted to put the winery for sale at auction once again. When I heard about it, I realized that she wanted to wash her hands of the whole mess. It was my prayer that she could start over in Fort Worth.

The winery went out on auction again, and this time it sold for $1,000,000. This price was $1,500,000 below the appraisal thought it would bring. She left the auction crying, and I went after her. She told me she had been counting on the winery's selling for at least $2,000,000 to $3,000,000. That would have helped her get re-established.

She became so despondent that she went into deeper depression. She left me a voicemail saying she had left Cotton and wanted me to know how much she appreciated my help and support. I could not help but feel I had failed her. I had not been there for her when she needed me. It made me wonder if my dad had felt the same way when he could not be there for Mom and me.

Family and friends tried to find her. No one know where she went. I called her and found her phone was disconnected.

Three months later, she was found dead in Mexico. She had been so distraught that she never recovered. I was not shocked. My time with her family at the funeral was bittersweet. They reassured me that Claire was now in a better place in Heaven where there is no more sorrow or pain. I just wish she could have had that here on Earth.

Chapter 16

The new owners were wine and vineyard brokers from Idaho. They hoped to own the winery a few years and then flip (sell) it and make a bundle. They knew they had purchased the winery below market value and knew me through the auctioneer because I had been at every auction. The auctioneers would say, "If you want to know something about Cotton, call Trevor." After several conversations, they kept me on part time, to take care of the few barrels left.

They told me this was going to be an easy and quick flip. They were accustomed to vineyard property that sold for hundreds of thousands of dollars per acre. They knew they had to have wine to sell and vineyards that produced grapes. That year, a spring freeze hit the growers of the Texas Panhandle, so there were no Texas grapes available to purchase to make wine. The estate vineyard produced nothing. Since there were no Texas grapes available to purchase, the "flippers" bought wines from Italy and France in large bladders and shipped them to Texas. They were bottled at the winery to sell in the Tasting Room.

The "flippers" purchased wineries all over the world as investments. They were familiar with high quality wines that they could purchase at extremely low prices. The wines were of excellent quality, but the wine community of Cotton rejected it.

The "flippers" claim to fame was when they bought Suue Ein Vineyards, a high-end winery known for producing Cabernet Sauvignon. They purchased the winery, held it for eighteen months and then doubled their money.

Other Texas wineries started talking badly about "the flippers," as they came to be known. Their focus was on buying and selling wineries. They were so used to flipping that they did nothing to promote events or take part in local events. They were outsiders from Idaho who did nothing to improve the grounds or work with the chamber of commerce. All the service organizations stopped having their weekly meetings there. The new buyers held the property for two years and sold it for $2,000,000. They made a quick million on the property and went back to Idaho.

The new buyer was Joey D., a retired distributor from San Antonio. He called me and said that the "flippers" had given him my name to help with the wine. He invited me out to dinner at the best Italian restaurant in town – Trattoria Messina.

Joey D. looked just like the Godfather in the movie. His hair was gray and slicked back tight to his skull. He had the biggest gold chain around his neck that I had ever seen, and his pinky ring had a huge diamond. Joey selected the table and told me that he had to sit with his back to the wall. "You know, it's an old habit from Chicago," he said.

Joey D. asked me, "Have you ever been to Chicago? That's where I'm from." I told him no, that I had never been but asked him what it was like to grow up in Chicago. Joey D. said, "I was FBI." I was surprised and asked if his family was in law enforcement. Joey D. laughed, "It means that I am Full Blooded Italian. Both my mother and father were born in Sicily and came to America. My father started a garbage collection company in Chicago." Joey D. told me that his first job was working at a local liquor store. "It's where I learned about wine," he said.

"I joined the air force and they shipped me to San Antonio. When I got out of the air force, I worked for a distributor in San Antonio. I saw the ad in the wine classified that this winery was for sale and I thought it would be a fantastic opportunity. With all my connections, I know I can re-establish wholesale distribution."

I wondered what those connections meant because I heard there was concern that he had mobster connections.

"Joey D. looked at me and said, "I am going to give you an offer you can't refuse." I wondered if I was going to be swimming with the fishes.

"I want you to oversee the wines that I will be purchasing. There are no Texas wines available. I discovered a loophole in the federal regulation that states a wine varietal name like Cabernet Sauvignon can be listed on the label without the appellation of origin (where the grapes grew) if it says, "For Sale in Texas Only.

"I contracted wineries in California to purchase Cabernet Sauvignon, Chardonnay, Pinot Noir, Sauvignon Blanc, and Merlot. I need you to offload the wines from tanker trucks into tanks. You and I can blend them and then you can arrange to get them bottled in Texas.

"I was able to obtain distribution in three major liquor-store chains in Texas. The wines were priced less expensively than comparable Texas wines and will be extremely popular, especially the Cabernet Sauvignon." Joey D. was right. The wines took off. They were extremely popular and got distribution in restaurant chains. The wines became so popular that a writer from Houston, Daisy Lee, came to Cotton to interview Joey D.

Daisy Lee asked, "What does 'For Sale in Texas Only" mean?"

Joey D. said, "It is a federal loophole that allows a winery to label the varietal without the appellation."

Daisy Lee responded, "Doesn't that misrepresent the origin of the wines?"

Joey D. explained, "It allows wineries who are short on grapes from an appellation to supplement with grapes from other appellations. Texas does not produce enough grapes for all the existing Texas wineries. It is not illegal."

Daisy Lee said, "It may not be illegal, but I think most Texans believe the winery did not have enough wine to distribute out of state, so they thought they had to buy it up before it was all gone. This could be why the wines are so popular."

Joey D. argued, "The reason the wines are so popular is because the price is right, and the quality is there."

Daisy Lee went back to her newspaper and wrote a scathing article about Joey D. Once the newspaper article explaining the federal loophole hit the market, it was picked up by all the other Texas newspapers.

Joey D's sales dried up and he told the distributor to close out the wines and get rid of them. The wines sold three for $10.00. Within twelve months, Joey D's plan failed.

The winery once again went up for sale, but the industry still had to resolve the issue of "For Sale in Texas Only." This exposure of the federal loophole gave rise to the "100% Texas Grown" wine movement. It was divisive for the industry.

We were fortunate to have a president of the Texas Wine and Grape Growers Association who was sensitive to this issue. I had met him at the association's annual meeting and had heard him speak on the issue. Under the leadership of President Paul Mitchell Bonarrigo, owner and Chief Executive Officer of Messina Hof Winery, the Texas Wine and Grape Growers Association developed the "100% Texas Grown" emblem for wines made from 100 percent Texas grapes. This was an encouraging beginning, but the state's grape shortages made it difficult for new wineries to obtain sufficient grape tonnage to reach the 100-percent-Texas mark so they could use the label. Grape production in Texas had not significantly increased in twenty years, yet the number of new wineries had increased 800 percent.

Chapter 17

The latest data shows that only California, Washington, and Oregon have more. Wineries have been popping up in North Texas along the Red River and East Texas as far east as Orange, Texas.

After John Ferris's work experience with the vineyards and wineries around the state, he went back to Texas A&M to help grow the number of acres of grapes in the state. On a trip there to visit him, he and I also visited Messina Hof Winery. We had a wonderful visit with Paul Mitchell Bonarrigo's parents, Paul V., and Merrill, who shared with me so much of the early history of the industry. I even got to spend time with Dr. McEachern. George Ray, as he asked me to call him, suggested that I consider coming to work with John on the new programs. He hinted that he might be retiring.

They all shared that in the early days of the Texas industry the laws supporting wineries had to overcome fierce resistance by the lobby group of the liquor store retailers. Fortunately, the Texas wine industry had support from the Speaker of the House Billy Clayton, who was a grape grower, and soon-to-be Speaker of the House Pete Laney, who was also a grape grower. It was fascinating that they were both grape growers for Messina Hof. Early grape growers like Bobby Smith, Bobby and Jennifer Cox, and Ed and Susan Auler, along with academic leaders like

Roy Mitchell, George McEachern, and Bill Lipe, helped to institute the Texas Farm Winery Act that supported Texas wineries.

Paul V. shared with us, "As the chairman of the Texas Department of Agriculture's Wine Advisory Committee, I made sure our industry voices were heard. We needed the Texas Department of Agriculture to be responsible for promoting Texas grape production and Texas wine. Susan Combs was the commissioner at the time. Her term of office saw a rapid amount of positive legislation, legislative market funding, and stimulation of positive enthusiasm for the wine industry." He went on, "She secured millions of dollars from the legislature for marketing and research. Extension personnel for viticultural and enology advisors were hired utilizing the legislative funding. Our first Texas enologist helped improve the quality of Texas wines." I have heard these were the glory days of the Texas legislature.

He explained that when Susan Combs spoke before the legislature, they listened to the needs of the Texas wine industry. "Under her leadership, Texas wines began to be served at the Texas State Fair and at the Texas Governor's Ball." Can you imagine the Texas State Fair ever serving any wine other than Texas? Appalling.

Paul regretted that when she left office, most of the funding was eliminated by the Texas Legislature. We have not had another Texas Agricultural Commissioner who was able to restore the millions of dollars of funding needed to support Texas wine.

In recent years, weather, injury, and herbicide overdrift have created their own evil spells on the industry. Sixty wine grape growers sought $560,000,000 in damages to their grape crops from Bayer-Monsanto. They alleged that Bayer's herbicides were drifting into their vineyards and were damaging crops. I can attest that I have seen herbicide damage to every grape crop on the Texas High Plains.

Fortunately, Texas wine quality has significantly improved, but distribution increases have not kept up. You will not find it in all stores, and most times inventory in the stores is extremely limited. As John and I predicted, successful wineries have established large wine ship clubs. It is giving them the opportunity to educate directly. Many are reserving their best wines for their VIPs. Varietal diversification has introduced new varieties such as Sagrantino, Tannat, Tempranillo, and more.

Acceptance of Texas wine has dramatically improved even in the brief time I have been involved. In the early '80s, Texas wine was a novelty. They called it a "Pet Rock." Now Texas wine is accepted by 30 to

40 percent of the wine public. We are starting to get respect. In the '80s, when a Texas winery won a gold medal, it made national news. News about medals today is harder to find. We cannot rely on medals for sales. We need to focus on educating the wine consumer on the quality of Texas wine.

As I look at Texas agriculture, our grapes and wine are the greatest success stories we can share. Texas winery owners like the Bonarrigo family inspired me. They have been judges in California wine competitions and lecturers of international marketing in England, Italy, France, Portugal, and the Republic of Georgia. They are dedicated to educating the world about Texas wine.

While expertise was growing, there were too many failures and bankruptcies. This lack of recognition stimulated my curiosity even more. What I witnessed with Equoni Winery was unprecedented. I had not heard of any winery anywhere that had gone through so many bankruptcies and foreclosures. It was like Equoni was cursed.

Chapter 18

Joey D's failure was the end for me. I knew it had to be more than bad luck that Equoni had so many failures, tragedies, and disappointments. What was going on with the property and in the industry? John and I talked extensively, "Is the land cursed?" "What was that mound in the backyard?" What does the Native American descendent know about this property?"

As I started to put the pieces together, I made an appointment with the adjacent property owner to find out the history of the winery property. The owner of the adjacent property to the winery was Paul Hawk. He was a Native American descendent of the Comanche tribe who had lived there on that land. The two of us began to communicate.

Paul attended Oklahoma State with a degree in Animal Science. He moved to Cotton after meeting his wife at Oklahoma State. She was from Cotton, and Paul's family had lived on the land as far back as anyone could remember and was highly respected by other members of his tribe. He said he was believed to have strong medicinal powers passed down from his descendants. Paul looked at me with an unemotional face and piercing eyes that made me feel he was looking through me. "My family's tribe has annual pow wows on the property. They wear their ceremonial costumes and re-enact traditions from the past." I was intrigued. By investigating deeper into Native American history, I would be able to find out more about my own family history.

Paul had four children and raised Painted Ponies. His ponies were considered the best in the USA.

I asked Paul Hawk why he thought so many of the owners of this winery had died. He responded, "Other than to sell water to the winery, no one ever bothered to talk to me. They never asked me about myself or about the history of the property. It was not my place to intervene in the winery operations. They had much heartache and grief." Paul asked me if I knew anything about the Comanche history in the Texas High Plains. I told him what I learned at Fort Sill. He asked me what I knew about Long Wolf. I had to say I knew nothing, but I was excited to learn about him and the Comanche. Paul seemed happy that I was interested in his ancestry.

Paul told me, "The earliest people of the Great Plains had hunted and gathered wild plants and hunted the American buffalo. They used every part to make items used in everyday life, such as food, cups, decorations, crafting tools, knives, and clothing. The tribes followed the seasonal grazing and migration of the buffalo. The Plains peoples lived in tipis because they were portable and allowed the nomadic life of following game." I admired that they lived such a sustainable lifestyle.

Paul spoke of the Comanche as tragic heroes. "They tried to protect the land. The European settlers attempting to colonize their territory were threats to the Comanche people. The Comanche were good trading partners but were feared for their raids against settlers in Texas. The settlers were slaughtering buffalo." The Comanche believed all the lands of the Southwest were their lands. They warred with everyone, including every other Native American tribe.

Several attempts at treaties failed. Then in 1845, when the Texas legislature refused to create an official boundary between Texas and the Comancheria, the treaty talks ended. The Comanche believed that they should have control over all lands in the Comancheria. The government, on the other hand, believed all the lands belonged to the New Republic and that the Native Americans should be relocated to Oklahoma.

Relationships with the Comanche were further strained due to a wave of epidemics from exposure to European diseases to which the Native Americans had no immunity. Smallpox, measles, influenza, and typhus fever arrived in America with the European explorers. These diseases ravaged the Comanche population. In some regions, the Comanche population was reduced by 90 percent. I knew some of my people must have been among them.

Paul went on, "When President Buchanan took office in 1857, he was determined to settle the land disputes throughout the Estacado. He placed General Ranald Slidell Mackenzie in charge of the cavalry. The general and cavalry were assigned to keep the peace between the Comanches and the United States government by force, if necessary.

"General Mackenzie was born in 1840 in New York City. He attended West Point, graduating in 1862 at the top of his class. During the Civil War, he was commissioned into the Union Army as a second lieutenant. His first assignment placed him at the Battle of Petersburg. A shell fragment ripped off two fingers on his right hand. The Native Americans referred to him as "Bad Hand."

In 1867 General Mackenzie oversaw the 41st Infantry. My dad said General Mackenzie's reputation in the historical records of the cavalry paint him as a compassionate leader.

During their tribal pow wows, Paul's people shared oral histories of these individuals. He said that Mackenzie's reputation was as an honorable soldier who was brave and respectful of the Native American tribes of the Southwest. Nevertheless, he did his duty in controlling the Native American conflicts by force. The Comanche leader in many of those conflicts was Long Wolf, son of Chief Ten Bears. Long Wolf and General Mackenzie struck a respectful relationship. Each of them was working diligently to keep the peace between the Comanche and newly arriving settlers.

Chapter 19

Like my own name, Talan, Native American names are fascinating to me. Why was he named Long Wolf? What does *Talan* mean? Paul said that names are important and speak to the spirit of the person. "At the mid-teen years, a young Native American man went on a vision quest, where he spent days in prayer and meditation, seeking the Creator's purpose for his life and a guardian spirit." The tribal stories told that the wolf was revealed as Long Wolf's guardian spirit. As Long Wolf's history unfolded for me, I came to respect the name he had been given. A wolf is independent and spends much time alone. Wolf is a name associated with courage, strength, loyalty, and success in hunting.

In my life, I respect the strength of family. I only wish I had a greater relationship with my father. Comanche boys not only identified with their fathers but with their father's family, with the bravest warriors in the band, and with the wisest of the tribe. Paul went on to say, "When we are five or six, we learn from our grandfathers to ride and shoot. The grandfathers also teach the stories of the families and the history and legends of the Comanche. Family celebrations are filled with stories of the past. This is how family legacy is passed to future generations." I wish my grandfather had been there longer in my life. I could have learned so much of our family history.

Paul added, "The medicine man usually assisted in the spirit quest. A medicine man is our counselor, the medical authority, and is considered prophet of the tribe. It is said that Long Wolf's Comanche medicine man was Brown Bear. He was a confidant of Chief Ten Bears and spiritual guide for Long Wolf." Paul continued, "One of Brown Bear's prophetic visions was that there would be unexpected hostility between the Comanche and the cavalry. Brown Bear had visions in his sleep of the cavalry not keeping their promises and of a time when they would slaughter his people."

"Long Wolf's father, Chief Ten Bears, was a strong advocate for making peace with the cavalry. He believed that by making peace he would be able to maintain the tribe's way of life for his people. Making war with the cavalry would have resulted in death to his people and a more rapid removal of his people from their lands and their way of life. The Comanche's salvation was to maintain a close relationship with General Mackenzie."

Paul said that one of the stories always shared at the pow wows was about the big black bear. "Long Wolf grew up as a young chief of his Comanche nation and was very respectful of his father, Ten Bears. Ten Bears had knowledge beyond his years. Once, when Long Wolf and Ten Bears were on a scouting trip in West Texas, known as the Territory of Fort Tahoka, they came upon a big black bear. It was dusk.

Shadows made it difficult to see. Ten Bears motioned to Long Wolf to move quietly and to put the food in slings up in the trees. As they raised the last food into the tree, the huge black bear charged at them. Long Wolf's instinct was to run as fast as possible. Ten Bears stood strong and commanded Long Wolf to stop. Long Wolf obeyed. Just as he did, he saw Ten Bears thrusting his spear into the big black bear's massive chest. Ten Bears stood his ground and saved the food and Long Wolf."

I thought about how special that meal must have been. Ten Bears not only saved the food in the tree but had produced new food from the big black bear. Native Americans never wasted anything. The Earth and everything in it were sacred.

"Long Wolf tanned the bear skin and made it into a ceremonial headdress costume to commemorate the day. They took bones and teeth to the village for use as tools. Long Wolf hung three of the bear's large teeth around his neck. He wore this necklace sacredly. It reminded him of the hunt with his father and the lessons learned from him."

Paul went on to explain that the original efforts to come to agreement on a treaty were difficult. "General Mackenzie offered unlimited hunting and protection of the buffalo in exchange for peace and release of Native American prisoners. But cavalry soldiers who hated the Comanche conducted unauthorized cavalry raids when General Mackenzie was out of the territory.

"Usually, the cavalry would steal horses and sometimes Native American women. Sometimes they would kill natives who resisted. The cavalry soldiers did not approve of General Mackenzie's negotiations. These unauthorized cavalry raids led to massacres of Native American villages. One raid was different.

"Cavalry soldiers raided the village to steal horses. They were dressed as Apache warriors. Chief Ten Bears heard the horses as they were being taken away. He approached the soldiers and, as he did, one of the soldiers shot Ten Bears and stole his necklace as a souvenir. It had been handed down to him.

"In this raid, Chief Ten Bears was killed. His son Long Wolf, who was now the new chief, was outraged and became even more suspicious. He demanded a response from the government. During the investigation, the United States government blamed the Apache for the massacre. Long Wolf did not believe it was the Apache, but he needed proof."

Paul said that the cavalry often tried to divide tribes by blaming one tribe against the other for cavalry atrocities. The story on the death of Ten Bears made me sick. I could not imagine the self-restraint Long Wolf had when he heard of the murder of Ten

Bears. I could not imagine my having that much restraint.

Paul continued, "Long Wolf was very respectful of Ten Bears and wished to honor him with a traditional burial ceremony. Ten Bears' body was wrapped in a blanket and placed on a horse behind a rider. The rider took the body to the highest point of the village, placed the body on the ground, and covered it with a massive earth mound. Then they placed stones found at the site around the edge of the mound. All of Ten Bears' possessions were burned on top of the burial mound out of respect and so that they would follow him to the afterlife. Lone Wolf noticed that Ten Bears necklace was missing. Ten Bears always wore that necklace. Lone Wolf took his knife blade and cut both his forearms to express his grief.

"Ten Bears was buried, and the tribe celebrated his life for thirty days. During this thirty days, Long Wolf visited the accused Apache tribe to discuss the massacre. The tribes, both known for their fighting prowess, hated each other so much that Long Wolf had to come with peace offering. The Apache had respected Ten Bears and received Long Wolf and his men. Together they discovered that the massacre had been staged by a cavalry unit dressed as Apache. General Mackenzie did his own investigation. He, too, believed Sergeant Little, a well-known

Comanche hater, and three other troops had conducted the massacre. They had stolen Apache clothing and murdered Ten Bears. General Mackenzie was told by Long Wolf that Ten Bears' necklace was removed from his body. General Mackenzie noticed the necklace hanging from Sergeant Little's neck.

"General Mackenzie held a trial, found them all guilty, and had them executed before a firing squad. General Mackenzie's punishment was swift, to discourage other cavalry from unauthorized raids on Native American tribes."

Paul Hawk's grandfather had been at the trial and had shared at the pow wow what he observed. He said that he watched in silence from the back of the crowd. General Mackenzie rode to meet Long Wolf to express his sorrow for the incident and explain how he dealt with Sergeant Little and his men. General Mackenzie offered the Medicine Lodge Treaty, promising churches, schools, and lands where the Native Americans could hunt, and he promised protection of the buffalo.

Paul continued, "Long Wolf met with the medicine man Brown Bear to receive his counsel. Brown Bear advised that they should no longer trust the cavalry. Together they took the meat of a buffalo and held it up to the sky, chanting "Sun (*Taabe*), Moon (*Mua*), Water (*Paa*), Man (*Tenahpu*)." Then they buried it in the ground as an offering to the Great Spirit for wisdom in dealing with the United States government and cavalry.

"Long Wolf tried to make peace with the Apache to create a united front against the cavalry, but the Apache had no interest in that. The Apache continued to attack the settlers as they arrived. The United States government became increasingly more desperate to make peace with the Comanche to minimize their attacks on settlers. This way they could focus on the Apache and not have to worry about the Comanche.

"Once President Buchanan heard of the Medicine Lodge Treaty and how General Mackenzie had dealt with Sergeant Little, he put General Philip Sheridan in charge of negotiations. Buchanan was concerned about the way the negotiations would go, and he felt that Mackenzie was weak and cared too much for the Comanche. Washington transferred General Mackenzie to inspect Fort Clark in Del Rio, Texas, and Fort Concho in San Angelo. President Buchanan's desire to settle the West gave no regard to the tribes that were displaced.

"The President told Sheridan to award Long Wolf, in the presence of his tribe, a presidential medal. The President hoped that this medal would pacify Long Wolf's desire for revenge. Presidents used these presidential medals as tokens of honor and respect.

The Native Americans received the medals with honor."

Paul said that his people viewed this medal as a major turning point in Native American and cavalry relations, but the real purpose of the medal was so the President would be able to control the Comanche nation and get them moved. The intention was to have a slow, twenty-five-year, orderly withdrawal of the Comanche from the High Plains to Oklahoma reservations.

"General Sheridan sent a telegram to General Mackenzie asking him to approach Long Wolf about the presentation," Paul Hawk said. "General Sheridan knew that Long Wolf trusted General Mackenzie and would not be suspicious of the medal's real intentions." I found myself rooting more and more for Long Wolf.

"Mackenzie returned to Cotton, and together Mackenzie and Sheridan made the invitation to Long Wolf. Suspicious of General Sheridan's intent, Long Wolf gave his thanks and graciously invited the generals and their men to dinner with the tribe.

"Long Wolf and the tribe members planned an elaborate ceremony and meal. The Comanche women were to prepare the meal of buffalo, grains, corn, and wild berries. They wore their best deerskin

dresses with flared skirt and beaded top with
buckskin fringes along the sleeves and hem.

"The Comanche men wore beaded shirts, leggings
with buckskin fringe, and animal fur. For the
ceremony, they donned their heavy robes made from
buffalo hides and wore their ceremonial headdresses
of eagle feathers. Long Wolf wore the bearskin
headdress he had fashioned from the black bear his
father Ten Bears had killed. Long Wolf even wore
the necklace of Ten Bears that had been returned to
him by General Mackenzie. Every element of the
dress and the dinner spoke to the Comanche culture,
heritage, and the lands they stewarded.

"General Sheridan, General Mackenzie, and Long
Wolf walked up to the burial ground. The Generals
paid respects to Ten Bears. There, in the presence of
his father's spirit, Long Wolf received the medal and
agreed in good faith that his tribe should sign the
treaty."

Paul Hawk told the story his grandfather had told
him. "Long Wolf introduced his entire family to
General Sheridan and General Mackenzie. The
mother of Long Wolf was Wise Hawk. She was the
teacher of the Comanche nation. She taught Long
Wolf to always see the good in people. She taught
her people to speak English. She knew that the white
settlers would not stop settling in the area, so
speaking their language would facilitate the
transition.

"The wife of Long Wolf, Shining Star, was the most beautiful Comanche in the tribe. Long Wolf fell in love with her the first time he saw her. Her dark black hair and dark eyes were like shining starlight in the north sky. Long Wolf and Shining Star had three children: Running Bull, Singing Water, and Walking Tall. Running Bull distrusted General Sheridan, hated the cavalry, and refused to eat with them, vowing revenge for his grandfather Ten Bears. Singing Waters was the peacemaker. Walking Tall was the future leader of the Comanche tribe. He was the smartest and most creative of the three children.

"Chief Long Wolf signed the treaty, as his father had desired, and proudly walked out of the ceremonial tent holding the treaty in the air for all his people to see and said, 'I lead my people into the light.'

"The Comanche and cavalry experienced seven years of peace while the cavalry focused its attention on the Apache."

Chapter 20

Unfortunately, the government did not prevent the slaughter of the buffalo herds as promised. Settlers killed large herds of buffalo to sell their hides and meat to other settlers. The Comanche reacted out of frustration and went on the offensive. In 1871, Mackenzie found himself once again at war. He suffered wounds for his seventh time at the Battle of Blanco Canyon, when the Comanche led by Running Bull defeated the cavalry and the troops retreated to Fort Griffin.

Pressures increased. The cavalry increased its attacks. Running Bull retaliated in 1874 by killing the settlers responsible for the buffalo killings in the Texas Panhandle. Running Bull's attacks did not have Long Wolf's permission. This was a disaster for the Comanche nation. The United States Army was called in to the area to retaliate and to drive Running Bull and his followers out of Texas and into Oklahoma. General Mackenzie and his troops destroyed five Native American villages, culminating in the Battle of Palo Duro Canyon. On November 5 at Tahoka Lake, his men slaughtered 1,400 Native American horses in hopes it would convince all the tribes to stop attacking settlers and make peace.

Records show that Chief Quanah Parker of the Kwahadi band of Comanche Kiowa arrived at Fort Sill, where General Mackenzie was in command over the Comanche Kiowa and Cheyenne Arapaho reservations. He promised Chief Parker money and land in exchange for peace and returning to the reservations permanently.

Paul Hawk said he knew General Mackenzie had a profound respect for Native Americans. He felt bad for him because his orders often created internal conflict. He was an obedient soldier who was emotionally troubled by what he had been ordered to do. He experienced mood swings and depression.

Long Wolf reached out to his old friend, asking for the two of them to make peace, but Mackenzie was unable to help. Mackenzie sent a note back stating that the President had put General Sheridan back in charge. General Sheridan sent a detachment led by Major Pope to talk with Long Wolf. As the detachment approached the village, a follower of Running Bull shot and killed Major Pope. Second in command, Lieutenant Stevens, saw Major Pope die right in front of him and was outraged. He lost all control and attacked and killed Long Wolf in retaliation.

Suddenly, both sides stopped and became silent. No one could believe what just happened. Long Wolf was gone. The medicine man Brown Bear witnessed the killing. He looked around at the cavalry and at the Comanche. A loud screech came from his body as he fell to his knees next to Long Wolf's body.

Crying, he drew his knife, cut his arm in grief, and cut a lock of Long Wolf's hair. Brown Bear assembled the entire tribe. His eyes were red with fire. Tears ran down his face. His voice was loud and clear. As he laid a blanket over Long Wolf, he proclaimed, "This land is forever cursed. It will never bear fruit until the cavalry atones for this senseless injustice." He went on to curse all the cavalry, the white settlers, and the land where Long Wolf was executed. It became known as the "Curse of Estacado." Brown Bear taught the leaders of the tribes to share the story throughout the generations. Not only did the Comanche tribe members know the story, but the white settlers in the area knew it as well.

That land was east of Cotton. After the curse, the Comanche called it the "land of bad omen." On that site of Long Wolf's burial ground, the pastures were barren, and the grazing cattle died mysteriously. No trees ever grew on the land.

Paul Hawk expressed compassion for General Mackenzie. I sympathized with Mackenzie's guilt about Long Wolf. I went back to the library to learn more about the cavalry. There I found excerpts from General Mackenzie's diary. He wrote that he became increasingly depressed and that he had a recurring dream. This dream caused him to wake up with nightly cold sweats. In his dream, he invites Long

Wolf to his home and, feeling happy, he opens his door to invite him inside. Then suddenly, out of nowhere, one of his men shoots and kills Long Wolf. Nightmares led to drinking. Drinking led to depression.

His depression worsened, and in March 1884 he was medically retired from the Army due to mental illness. The Curse of Estacado had struck. In June 1884, he returned to New York so his sister could care for him. In 1886, he transferred to New Brighton Mental Institution on Staten Island. He died there in January 1889. His nightmares of Native American massacres and the murder of his friend Long Wolf wore on his conscience. He once confided to his sister how guilty he felt that he could not prevent Long Wolf's murder and about feeling responsible for the Curse of Estacado.

His faith and upbringing had taught him to love all humankind. He knew kindness and tolerance could have created such a different outcome. His friendship with Long Wolf could have prevented bloodshed and restored peace and a greater respect of Southwest Native Americans.

This was so much information that I did not expect. How could something that happened so long ago so dramatically affect the lives of people today? I was beginning to understand the events of the Estacado more clearly—the auctions, the bankruptcies, deceit of marriage, even the deaths of Equoni owners.

I felt like I needed to go to the winery. Driving out there, I thought about all that Paul Hawk had said. The sun was setting over the vineyard when I arrived, and it suddenly hit me. The Curse of Estacado happened on the land of Equoni Winery.

I had witnessed the destruction of so many people, all caused by the senseless murder of Long Wolf. The callous treatment of the Comanche by the cavalry led to Brown Bear's despair. His curse has continued until this day, and only the cavalry's apology could lift the curse. There was no way that would happen. I thought, *without that apology, the land of this winery will always be cursed.* Sadness and a sense of hopelessness overwhelmed me.

Chapter 21

After experiencing so much, and after learning so much about the Native American and Texas wine legacies, I also began to think about my own family heritage and wanted answers. Dad and I camped at Lake Texoma, where we had lots of time to talk. I told my dad about the story Paul Hawk had shared with me. I explained to him about Ten Bears, Long Wolf, Brown Bear, and the Curse of Estacado. My dad teared up. He admitted knowing his father was Comanche. I was shocked and disappointed. Why had he not told me?

His response was, "Discrimination against the Native Americans would have prevented me from promotions in the military. Please know that I am not ashamed of my heritage, but I wanted to provide the best for you and your mom." I studied his face. It softened as he looked at me. He went on, "Trevor, my army division is a cavalry division. We are the 1st Cavalry Division."

I was so confused but excited. He could see the surprise on my face. But that was just the beginning. He went on to tell me that our name *Talan* came from my grandfather's family. It turns out that my grandfather was Golden Hawk, but he had taken the name Talan in the military.

I asked him about his father. He said, "He passed away when you were four years old."

My dad said his heritage was Comanche! My grandfather was Comanche! Dad went on, "Your grandmother was of German ancestry. She came from St. Louis. Your granddad and grandmother met when he was training to be a Code Talker during World War II."

My father was not a man to show emotion, but his pride shown through when he shared that the enemy were never able to break the code. He told me that during the war, many Native American tribe members worked to convey secret coded messages in their own native languages.

My father said my grandfather rarely spoke of his native American upbringing. His family lived off the reservation, so he grew up in Lawton, Oklahoma, and went to Lawton High School. His basic training was at Fort Sill. He was assigned to the Marines in the South Pacific. He helped communicate secret messages in the native Comanche tongue. My grandfather was a code talker for the Marine Corps! From the South Pacific, he transferred to the European conflict and was part of the invasion force at D-Day. He was awarded a congressional medal and rose to the rank of Sergeant.

After the war, my grandparents married and settled on the west side of Lawton, where he worked as a welder.

They had one child, my dad. My dad went to Oklahoma State, where he enrolled in the Reserve Officers' Training Corps program. My mom was an English major with a minor in floriculture. They met and married. She became a teacher. Her training came in handy, because at every base where my dad was stationed, she taught English.

My dad went into the service in 1980 and retired as a Colonel in 2008. He entered the Army as a second lieutenant and was promoted quickly to Colonel. When Dad retired, he commanded the 1st Cavalry Division at Fort Sill. His men honored him at the change-of-command ceremony. He received gifts for his devoted service. I was so proud of him. I felt like I was just beginning to know my dad.

Mom and Dad settled in my granddad's homestead. After my grandfather died, my grandmother followed him to heaven six years later. My dad and mom raised cattle. Mom retired from teaching. The two of them are dedicated to each other and the land. It means so much to me to think of my own legacy and the Comanche heritage that runs through my veins.

After he shared all of this, my dad looked at me. I could see a sparkle in his eyes and a broad smile on his face. He said, "I was a cavalry officer. Do you think I could apologize for the cavalry and help make the necessary amends to remove the curse?" I told him it was worth a try.

He found his uniform and, much to our surprise, it still fit. He looked so strong. I made an appointment to see Paul Hawk. We arrived at his home. My dad was as diplomatic as I have ever seen him. He walked up to Paul Hawk in his full dress, highly decorated military uniform and said, "On behalf of the 1st Cavalry, I would like to extend our sincere apology for the murder of Long Wolf."

Paul had a tear in his eye. I could see that he never thought he would see such a day and so appreciated what my dad was willing to do. Paul asked us to wait in his living room. He went to his bedroom. I really did not know what to say to my dad. I felt so proud and so grateful for such a kind and respectful father.

Twenty minutes later Paul Hawk returned in full Comanche dress. He was now Paul Hawk, the medicine man of the Comanche tribe, and my dad represented the 1st Cavalry Division. The sun was setting over the vineyard of Equoni Winery. The sky turned blood red.

We got into his Jeep and drove up the mound which we now know is Chief Long Wolf's burial ground. Paul Hawk raised his arms to the heavens and spoke in Comanche. As he chanted loudly, we heard what sounded like a wolf howling. We looked in the direction of the sound and saw a wolf staring at us from the edge of the vineyard. He was howling with a shrill that filled the Estacado.

Paul turned to my dad and asked him to repeat his apology to Long Wolf and the Comanche tribe. My dad's booming voice cried out the Cavalry's sorrow for the murder of Long Wolf. He lamented this senseless injustice and asked forgiveness from the Great Spirit. Then, in Comanche, Paul Hawk declared the Curse of Estacado lifted. As he declared the curse removed, the wolf's howl softened, as though in acceptance. Then, just as the wolf had appeared, we saw it disappear into the vineyard. It was as though Long Wolf's spirit had been with us the entire time and could now rest in peace.

We returned to Paul's home and shared more stories of our past. When my dad shared that his father was Golden Hawk Talan, Paul touched his hand and said they were from the same tribe. My father looked shocked. Paul went on to say that the name Golden Hawk was a legend in his tribe. Golden Hawk's legacy of helping the Marines is still shared at pow wow.

As I look back on all that I have witnessed, I realize that deep hatreds are difficult to resolve. Our nation was settled by the wrongs that had been thrust upon

Native Americans. The Curse of Estacado resulted in many lives lost and many families destroyed. Now that the curse has been lifted, the Equoni winery should flourish. Time will tell. My time here at State is ending. I will be joining my friend John Ferry from Texas A&M University to teach Viticulture. John called me when his mentor Dr. George Ray McEachern retired to professor emeritus status. I was blessed and honored to be hired for his position. It will fun hearing more stories about the history of Texas grapes and wine. Joining the Texas A&M University faculty will provide me with the opportunity to learn about the history of grape growing and winemaking in the Brazos Valley dating back to the 1800's.

About the Authors

Paul V. and Merrill Bonarrigo founded Messina Hof Vineyard in 1977 in Bryan, Texas, as pioneers of the Texas grape and wine industries. Today, Messina Hof has four wineries around Texas and continues to be one of the most awarded wineries in Texas in regional, national, and international competitions. Today the Messina Hof legacy continues with their son, Paul, and his wife, Karen.

Paul V. Bonarrigo, born in the shadow of Yankee Stadium and graduated from Columbia University, served in the Navy during Vietnam, and studied winemaking at the University of California–Davis while stationed in California. Merrill Bonarrigo, a native of Bryan–College Station, Texas, graduated from Texas A&M University with a degree in business management.

Paul and Merrill introduced Sagrantino grapes to Texas, and they have traveled to thirty-eight countries to teach wine, hospitality, and successful generational transition. They lead wine tour groups around the world, blog, and write books:

Ultimate Food and Wine Pairing Cookbook

Ultimate Food and Wine Pairing Cookbook II

Vineyard Cuisine, Meals, and Memories from Messina Hof

Family, Tradition and Romance—The Messina Hof Story

Since 2015 Paul and Merrill have developed Messina Hof Estates, a 37-acre vineyard lifestyle community. For more information, visit TheVineyardDistrict.com.

CPSIA information can be obtained
at www.ICGtesting.com
Printed in the USA
JSRBC011125150922
30471JS00008B/28